# ERIC JOHNSON

# Emotional Eater

*How I lost 200 pounds and have kept it off for 20 years*

**PLATYPUS**

PUBLISHING

First edition

ISBN: 978-1-962133-10-4

This book was professionally typeset on Reedsy.
Find out more at reedsy.com

# Contents

# Preface

*To me, food is love. It's also romance. Intimacy and sex come to mind as well as I imagine how it feels in my mouth, touching my lips and sliding across my tongue. The particles mingle with my saliva as they hit my 10,000 taste buds, and because these taste buds regenerate themselves every two weeks, it's always new and exciting.*

*I kiss fudge. I have my way with cheesecake and mashed potatoes. I swoon over the gentle way food enters me, working its way inside, and then it explodes and changes my cells. It never leaves. The more I eat, the more it stays with me.*

*Food is everything to me.*

## I lost 200 pounds and I've kept it off for over 20 years. This is my story of how I did it.

Losing 200 pounds feels like the greatest thing I've done in my life. It's for sure the thing that makes me the happiest day in and day out. Being thin is the one thing I love more than food, which says a lot. Even at 170 pounds, food is my best friend and constant companion. It will forever be my true love.

When I was 50, 100, 200 pounds overweight, all I wanted was to be thin, though I never thought I could be. You see, I'm the biggest food addict I've ever met. If I were to throw in the towel, I could gain 100 pounds back in a year, no problem. I so understand what it's like to be very overweight and not be able to stop eating.

I'm obsessed with food. I can eat like no one I know. Sugar plum fairies really do dance in my head, and candy bars come to life like the old cartoons that would play in theaters before the movie. Cupcakes grow legs and run toward me. Doughnuts have personalities and potato chips are instant friends. I am constantly thinking about what I can eat next.

This obsession has caused me to do things I'm not proud of. I've roamed the halls of a hotel late at night, eating scraps off the room service trays left outside the doors. I've eaten doughnuts out of the garbage at work. (That *Seinfeld* episode when George does the same never struck me as that outrageous.) When I couldn't wait to cook it, I ate raw bacon like gummy worms. I've stolen money to buy cookies from the vending machine. Oh, the many bulk bins I've grazed on at the grocery store like they were free samples.

Even at 170 pounds, I'll stand in front of the refrigerator with the door open and eat five slices of bread like chips. When I'm at work, all I think about is heading to the kitchen to eat. I'll get something random from the cupboard, bring it back to my desk, and scarf it down. As soon as it's gone, I think about what I can get next.

The only difference between now and when I was a fat kid is what I eat and that I don't do it as often. Life as a grown-up ends up not much different than when I would run home from school after a bad day and eat everything in sight. Instead of sneaking back to the kitchen during TV commercials, it's between Zoom meetings.

## I'm an emotional eater

How are we emotional eaters supposed to get along without our best friend food? Not eating when stressed or scared or lonely or hurt is unthinkable to us. The compulsion to eat feels so much stronger than we are.

**As a food addict, I feel powerless under its spell. I don't want to overeat, but it's as if I can't help myself. Something inside makes me do it. When I'm insecure or bored, food is a companion and ally. Food is a dog, a best friend, a source of love. Food is the one thing that will never leave me.**

Compulsive eating soothes the hard edges of life. It talks me off the ledge and adds a little sparkle to the mundane. It's the most reliable thing in the world, and it always makes me feel better—for a little while.

Then the cycle begins. I eat a lot and then I feel bad about it because I want to be thin more than anything. This makes me eat more and then the fat begins to accumulate. Then I feel really, really bad.

I guess I'm a fat realist. I'm not sure any of us who turn to food for love, comfort, and security ever completely get over it. Food is forever a diva in my life. It's simply not going to be ignored. It's Barbra Streisand, Celine Dion, and Mariah Carey all rolled into one. As far as food goes, "Nobody puts baby in the corner." Food isn't going anywhere in my life, and it certainly isn't going easy.

So, what do I do? For one thing, I keep my old friend close by—but I've cleaned up his act. Dieting perfectionism sabotaged me over and over through the years. I finally faced the reality that my food compulsion may always be a part of me. I needed to find a way to get along with my food addiction so I could lose weight, the thing I wanted most in the world.

I still eat a lot when I need to, but I've upgraded from half a cake to half a watermelon, for example. I call it friendly bingeing. A bag of baby carrots has replaced a bag of Doritos. I'll eat grapes on the way home from the grocery store rather than a Milky Way bar. I tell myself I can eat all I want, but it needs to have at least some benefit to my body... or at least, not as much harm. This works most of the time.

## "I've been thin. I've been fat. Thin is better."

There's a lyric from the Broadway musical *A Class Act* that goes, "I've been thin. I've been fat. Thin is better." When I first heard it, I thought, yes, this Ed Kleban guy knows what he's talking about.

Being thin is so much better than being fat, though saying it out loud feels not quite right. It's like I'm not supposed to think or feel or certainly speak it. If we say aloud that we'd rather be thin, it seems vain and self-centered. Plus, it draws attention to our trying to lose, and ugh, it's so disappointing and embarrassing when we don't.

> **But I'll say it again: being thin is so much better than being fat. Fat makes life harder. Of course, not all your problems go away when you lose weight, but many do, and life is generally so much easier.**

I don't believe that anyone is happy being fat. I surely never was. I had moments, but they were fleeting. Again, this is my experience, but I often notice overweight folks tugging at their clothes and plastering on smile masks with eyes that look dead inside. I see them scan a room to find a chair that won't break, and my heart hurts for them. I've been there. I broke a bed at a friend's house when I was 18 and another time at my cousin's when I was 12. Once, a theater seat folded beneath me during one of the 45 times I saw *Flashdance*. I split many pairs of pants in public. I hope all the fat people out there can feel a certain level of self-love. I so hope they do. I couldn't, but I did find it along the way, and I find it so much easier at 170 pounds to love myself, warts and all.

I've had conversations with friends or co-workers who are carrying extra pounds, and at first they'll play it cool when it comes to their weight. Then we'll talk some more, and soon their frustration over their weight and their desire to lose it surfaces.

**Being thin helps me feel comfortable in my skin, which is what it's all about.**

Stepping out of the shower and not hating what I see (though I may not love, love, love it every time) clears so much emotional garbage out of the psyche.

Not having that self-loathing, and the hundreds of extra pounds, simply lightens the load of living. For this alone, I would love everyone who needs to lose weight to make it a priority. Yes, loving yourself when you're heavy is possible, but it's so much easier at 170. I could never get there when I was in the 200 and 300s.

Losing weight may require eliminating things in life that make you turn to food. This can be challenging because it might be something big like a job or a relationship. The most important thing is to find a way to get on with it, even if you're not in the place to make that big leap. I can testify that whatever you have in your life that is making you eat will be easier to deal with after you've lost some weight. Even 10 pounds lost begins to clear the storm clouds.

## The F-word

It also feels a little wrong to say fat, but please know I use the word lovingly. I was 380 pounds at my heaviest, and I was the one who didn't fit into the rollercoaster seat. I've done the walk of shame past the queue of skinny people staring at me, some giggling and smirking. Those of us who've been fat may use the word, but if you haven't, proceed with caution. If you've been there, you know that nothing describes the stuffed, awkward, uncomfortable feeling of extra weight like the word fat. The word, well, it just sounds fat.

I also use the word fat rather than chubby, fluffy, or "more-to-love" because these all dance around the issue and try to lessen the impact it has on life, both the quality and quantity. We use those words because they hide our shame, but they keep us from facing the reality of carrying many extra pounds. How many fat people over 80 do we see? I recall a giant scale somewhere that you'd slip a quarter into, step on, and get your weight, along with a fortune. This says it all. Our weight says so much about what our future can hold for us. Fat keeps us from our hopes and dreams. Not only are our lives less full and rich than they could be, they are also shorter.

## Then there are all the diets and weight loss programs out there

I get frustrated with all the weight loss programs and diets that never get to the heart of the matter. They always skip the chapter explaining why we can't stop eating. We pay our money, behave like good little kids for a while, and then we start slipping and sliding. Our inner fat kid wins. We want to believe the TV commercials, Facebook ads, and fitness magazines at the grocery checkout, which I still impulsively grab. "Lose weight for good" gets me every time. We search endlessly for the miracle, the answer, the one diet that will change our lives. (Side note: I don't think we should have to pay a lot of money to lose weight.)

> **The plans and programs work at first. They're great at getting us started and I would even encourage you to use one if you need to get the weight loss ball rolling (but please, don't fork over a lot of cash).**

The Weight Watchers app helped me drop my final 10 pounds and figure out how much I could eat in a day to stay around 170. The free Lose It app is also a great way to touch base with the number of calories we need to lose and maintain. I go back to it when I've gained a few pounds and I need a reset. The science is black and white—you can find out how to lose weight with a Google search—but the science is such a tiny part of it.

It's easy to be successful for a while. The newness carries us when we start a diet or weight loss regime. Soon the excitement fades, and we are again left with the frustration of "Why do I eat when I don't want to?" The cookies start to tug at our sleeves.

> **Why does the emotional and compulsive eater inside us win? That is the code we must crack.**

*This book tells how I did it. This is my food story.* As you read, you will see my journey was not a straight and steady path; there were many twists and turns and bumps along the way. This is how it goes for most of us, I believe. Discovering why we turn to food can be a two-steps-forward-one-step-back process, but that's how I got to the heart of my emotional eating.

> **In addition to losing weight, I discovered how to get along in the world as a highly sensitive, people pleasing, compulsive eater. I even found my own personal secret to happiness.**

## Hearing other people's stories may be the only thing that helps

Something needs to click inside us. I think that's why most programs fail in the long run—the internal click doesn't happen. The overeater hasn't figured out why they can't stop when all they want to do is lose weight.

Outside support can help, but losing weight is mostly an inside job. Hearing how others did it helps the most, I think.

> **Nothing is better than hearing someone else's story and thinking, "Wow, I see myself in you." It helps me feel more okay with myself.**

Hearing another story like mine validates that what I went through was hard, which is why I responded the way I did. I'm not a solitary freak or a one-off in the world. I was just doing my best.

Not feeling alone in whatever we are going through is always key. When I hear someone else who has gone through what I did—especially when we have something in common, like gender, age, sexuality, or where we grew up—I feel not so alone. It's like someone sees me and says, "Me too. I understand." I feel seen and understood.

This is how I felt when I heard a fellow addict talk about chewing his nails as a little boy to distract and disassociate from his dad's hurtful words and looks. He also spoke of the intense anxiety he felt going to college, with the swarms of people all around, and the energy of competition, grading, passing, and failing. It was like his words were coming out of my mouth.

Witnessing someone who has gone through what I have and reacted the same way, relieves the shame and regret. It somehow detoxifies it all and I feel better about the experience. When I hear a story like mine, I think, "Well, of course, I ate like a house on fire. Anybody would have." By witnessing someone with a similar story, we can view our situation objectively and with the compassion we rarely give ourselves.

## Please, make it a priority

I'm the lightest I've been since fifth grade. At 58, I feel better than I ever have.

People often ask me how I lost the weight, especially those who knew me at 280 and above. I'm not a weight-loss doctor or a nutritionist or a therapist, though I feel I have a DIY PhD in all three. In the end, I only know what has worked for me, and I want this for anyone who is fat. I really, really want this for you. And I want it for you now. I've never liked the phrase, "If I can do it, anyone can." It's so self-deprecating and usually not true. That said, I wholeheartedly believe if I can lose weight, you can too.

I will attest that with every year, the body clings more desperately to the pounds. They tell us our metabolism slows yearly, even with continued exercise. I say to all you 20- and 30-somethings, lose the weight now.

**I hope that what I've learned along the way will help you get on with it because nothing is better than being thin.**

Though eating runs a close second.

# I

# Part One

*How to gain 200 pounds*

# Chapter 1

I bundled up in my old barn coat that no longer reached across my stomach. Then I slipped on a pair of old sneakers with the heel flattened like a clog, and slid and meandered my way down the lonely old path to the barn that no one walked any longer. Funny, it had been used for so many years, it was almost as if the snow didn't collect on it, like it was hot from so many emotional trips back and forth. A two-foot snowbank flanked a tiny valley so narrow it was like walking a tightrope. I was on a lonely and anxious circus walk to weigh myself on the giant feed scale, like a big bag of corn or maybe a calf that was being sold off.

I had made many walks like this through the years. The terrifying walk to PE class and down the hall in high school was a slow rug burn and constant stomachache. I had walked through the fires of hell as a teenager, so a few minutes in the Minnesota below-zero night was nothing. The moon was so bright and blue, it made sure I could see ahead of me, and that I didn't feel so alone.

The old milk room of the barn still smelled sweet and dusty, like manure and hay. I dropped my coat and sweatpants and pulled off my enormous t-shirt the size of an old lady's nightgown. I slid my underwear down and kicked them across the freezing cement floor and stepped up on the platform, like I had many times.

Clunk, the arm dropped. I was way above where I was at my last weigh-in. I slid the cold metal bar to the right, and I could feel my heartbeat in my teeth. I slid it more. The arm finally balanced; it swung gently like a dancer. It moved like the dancer I knew I was, who also danced around things in life.

3

There it was. I did it. I made it to 380 pounds.

"It's okay, Eric. You're okay. You'll be fine." I kept repeating it in a panic, and then I turned on myself. I began to slap my big boobs and Santa belly and lumpy thighs and big pillow butt like I was killing imaginary bugs.

Maybe Mom would help me lose weight this time; she had promised once when I had chest pains that were likely indigestion. But no one would or could save me—this I knew from experience. I did this to myself. I was responsible for it. I was an adult now—18 years and four months old—so if anything was going to change, it had to be me who did it.

\* \* \*

I imagine that in the nine months I grew in my mom's stomach, I fed off not only what she ate, but how she felt about it and why. A bag of Bugles chewed into a gritty paste calmed her nervous stomach. Crunchy chocolate-covered peanut clusters lifted her spirits. My personality was basically formed off her sneaking Kraft caramels from a cookie jar and thinking that no one could hear the noisy cellophane as she opened them. Several years later, I'd tiptoe into the kitchen for more Oreos, thinking I was invisible, and I'd hear, "Yes, Eric, I see you."

Half a century later and in my 50s, I'm still sneaking into the kitchen to steal bites of something even when no one is around. I ask myself, "Who am I hiding it from?" I seem to be hiding it from myself because even at 170 pounds, I'm still embarrassed by my addiction to food.

Maybe my perspective was made hazy by the cigarettes Mom chain-smoked during her pregnancy. It relaxes the mother, they told her, and the constant need for something big and vague grew in me with each inhale. Perhaps some of the beer my dad loved to drink was in his sperm and landed in me, and I was born just the tiniest bit buzzed.

My nine months in the womb were one big college party I didn't want to end, and that's how I see eating to this day.

I don't want the feelings that go along with food to stop. Not long ago, I was eating pudding, and I thought, nothing bothers me when I do this. This is how I want to feel all the time.

## The magical powdered sugar doughnut

It was a Saturday morning when I was four. I was alone, as I always seemed to be, except for the lovely box of doughnuts on the coffee table. It was that magic trio: the chocolate-covered, the crunchy one, and the one dusted with powdered sugar.

Ah, the powdered sugar doughnut. It was cocaine to a little fat kid. I picked it up, and the mere contact gave me a rush. When I bit into it, the magic dust sprinkled down, releasing a type of feel-good drug into the air and into my system. It covered the front of my fat kid sweatshirt like frost does on a windshield on a cold morning in Minnesota.

The messiness of this enchanted white doughnut didn't bother me. This was my destiny: to be covered, almost anointed with my food. The feeling of relaxed euphoria was so intense it's still with me fifty years later, and in a way, I think I've been trying to get that hit ever since.

## But then I was nearly killed by a Dairy Queen vanilla malt

On one of our family's special trips to the Twin Cities that farm kids live for, our Ford Galaxy 500 overheated, as it always seemed to do. We stopped at the Dairy Queen in the southern suburb of Chaska to let it cool down, and I was so excited I shot out of the car as soon as the wheels stopped.

I wedged my chubbiness into the Formica booth and waited for my skinny dad to bring straws, spoons, and napkins. Mom set my big vanilla malt in front of me at eye level; it was a little Mount Everest to me. The waxy cup clicked on the table, and something clicked in me. One of the harsh fluorescent lights shone directly on it, and it seemed to sparkle. I had experienced the thick sweetness before, and they made the cup so irresistible with the naughty little Dennis the Menace running wildly on the side. Even at five, I knew this was a hefty serving of feeling good.

I couldn't take it any longer. I flicked off the flimsy lid, wrapped my little fingers around the bottom, and tipped it up to my mouth. As you can imagine, the whole thing poured down like lava into my nose and mouth and down my shirt, and it piled up on my little belly. I was, quite literally, smothering. I gasped for air like a fish out of water and flailed my arms like I was drowning because I sort of was. My eyes began to water the way they do when you're about to cry.

Mom scooped the ice cream out of my nose and my mouth, her fingers so far back they were choking me, and I sat in a type of shock and red-faced humiliation as I came back to earth. It was a food slap in the face, an ice cream punch to the nose.

That about summed up the next 25 years or so of my eating.


## The F-word

Mom said at least a dozen times to me through the years: "Until you were five, you were this big around," and she made the "OK" gesture with her hand. A cigarette was usually propped between two of her fingers. I've seen photos, and this isn't exactly the case; I could have been Pugslie's stand-in on *The Adam's Family. She* may not have been the most impartial judge at 200 and some pounds (think Melissa McCarthy in *Bridesmaids*). I started to hear the hideous F-word (fat) from the other kids once I headed off to school in nearby Arlington, Minnesota (population 1,700 or so), so I must have been at least somewhat fat for my age.

The F-word. I've embraced it now, and because I was fat for so much of my life, I get the unique privilege of being able to use it freely. I have the accreditation. It can be fun to watch those who haven't been there struggle to say it. To pause and then elongate the F, then freeze in a chipmunk face to test if they should finish. They are right. If you've never been fat, watch your mouth.

## Sugar soothed me when the world (and my dad's words) stung

I was sitting alone in the barn as I often did, and I was belting out my own little opera with the 25 or so barn cats we always had. One had what looked like cauliflower growing out of its ear. I keened. I wailed. I boo-hooed high and quivery over and over again like an old lady in the church choir. The late afternoon sun cut through the dusty air that smelled rather sweet from dry hay and cow manure, and just as the beam of light struck my face, I hit high C at full voice.

"Eric, shut up." I didn't know Dad was there. He snapped inside and then snapped at me. He couldn't take it anymore. Who wouldn't have been a little edgy when you have your arm up a cow's butt, and your five-year-old boy is doing his best Beverly Sills in the corner? It stung bad, probably more than it should have, and I remember it like it was yesterday's evening news. I was such a sensitive little kid.

> **I found my way to the house and into the kitchen. The sugar bowl sat in the cupboard above the coffee maker and I took a teaspoon out of the silverware drawer and fed myself spoonful after spoonful, at least 25 in steady succession, as if a metronome was keeping time.**

I thought no one would notice if I never took the bowl off the shelf. If no one knew, in a way, it didn't even happen. Somehow, the secret was even more satisfying. It was as if I was magically invisible.

When the pretty little granules like new snow landed on my tongue, it was all fizzy and fun. It was Saturday morning cartoons, and I would soar like

I was on a rollercoaster or a merry-go-round at the dusty and dirty little county fair in our town. My big, strong dad, who loved me perfectly, would lift me into his arms, while all around was a carnival with colorful horses leaping in a circle, in opposition to the direction my dad and I were spinning, as he lifted me even higher, and twirled me around and around. Then the calm washed over me, and it didn't matter that the fair or carnival wasn't real. It felt good and safe and happy, and I drifted off to the living room and fell into the big cushy chair in front of the TV. I played with Sigmund and the Sea Monsters, Laverne and Shirley, Fonzie, and Mork from Ork, who really did seem to love fat, shy, sissy little farm boys.

# Chapter 2

## The Fat Kid's Club

There's a secret society out there. You may already belong and don't even know it. We don't have monthly meetings or secret handshakes, but we've definitely paid our dues. There are no membership cards, but we know each other when we meet on the street or in the lunchroom at work.

It's the fat kid's club.

> **We are the kids who grew up fat, heard fatso a lot, and suffered the slings and arrows of being different. Perhaps we didn't get fat until later in life, but something happened to us when we were young that makes us want to eat all the time as adults.**

Cookies soothe feelings of not being good enough at work. Birthday cake is something we would be happy with every day of the year when life seems so blah. We sometimes do disgusting things, like eat a perfectly good doughnut out of the garbage at work. We don't want to, but we know it's a temporary hit of feeling good, and that's all that matters sometimes.

Sometimes we manage to hide our membership in the club. We don't sport the blazer with the badge on the pocket. It shocks me when people think of me as a skinny guy. No one would think, oh, look at that big fat guy, but I still feel chubby and afflicted and a little broken inside. I swear, once a fat kid, always a fat kid.

If you keep your eyes open, you see a lot of us running around. We fidget, tug at our shirts, and adjust our jackets a lot. Maybe we tie sweatshirts around our waists to hide our butts. You can hear our nervous laughs and witness a need to please and be liked.

We do, on some level, always carry our heaviest weight. It's an invisible parka with weights sewn in. Skinny jeans may go on my body now, but I'll always walk in them like they have a red tag on the pocket that reads, I shouldn't be wearing these.

The famous and the gorgeous are not immune. I remember reading an interview with Channing Tatum, that beautiful gift-from-God movie star. It was when the first *Magic Mike* movie about male strippers came out. Many of us—straight, gay, male, female—marveled at his abs, the square jaw, and the perfectly shaped butt like giant scoops of ice cream. He swaggered around in a G-string up on the screen like he owned the place.

In the interview, he talked about his inner 14-year-old fat boy. He said he can't stop eating when he isn't making a movie, and you can see when he does the rounds on the talk shows and at the Oscars, he fills out a little. His cheeks get very full, his neck gets very thick, and his suit jacket doesn't quite close.

I also study actor Chris Pratt, who lost 50 or so pounds a few years ago and bulked up with lots of muscles. Now he's a hunky leading man, but I still sense the little fat boy.

When he was on the cover of *People* magazine, nipped out in a pool wearing a tank top, something seemed a little off. He didn't look entirely comfortable, almost like he would prefer to be in a Hawaiian shirt floating on an innertube.

On *Live with Kelly*, he kept tugging at his jacket like he was covering up a belly that happened over the summer. When he hosted *Saturday Night Live*, he sported a skinny suit and didn't seem comfortable; he was struggling in this second, awkward skin that was the very tight suit, and I bet he would have preferred to be in baggy khakis with a sweatshirt tied around his waist.

I've tied a lot of sweatshirts around my waist through the years. You might think it was when I was heavy, but not necessarily. There is still nothing like an extra layer of fabric around my equator to make me feel safe and protected from the world and the judgmental eyes of others. I like to cover the area where I was punched a lot in high school. If this is a thing for you, it can happen as much at 170 as 380.

## I can't take off my clothes in front of other boys!

The locker room seems to be a dreaded place for most kids. When you're a little Pillsbury dough boy, and an especially sensitive one, a locker room is a death zone. I was a pudgy butterball at nine, with little boy breasts. My body was a cream puff, and public nudity was as terrifying as the horror movies I watched 12 inches from the TV screen. But there was no option. In the 1970s, there was no locker room conscientious objecting.

Mr. Nyquist made us shower naked, but at least I could hide my stuff by holding my suit in front of me. I had to hide my penis in the shower. I was ashamed of the poor little thing because it hid, too, like a Chapstick turned in. Glendon Jacobus yelled, "Look, he doesn't have a weenis." Glendon, you little dumbshit, of course I had one; it was just covered up by all the fat.

We slipped and slid on the tile to meet up with the girls, and everyone got to see each other. This probably wasn't any big deal if you were a normal-sized kid, but I waited for someone to point and yell, "Look, his boobs are bigger than the girls," which they were. I was the most well-developed in the class.

When you are a boy with boobs, the boobs walk in the room first and have a neon arrow pointing to them, at least in your head. My boy boobs weighed 75 pounds in my mind and were a big part of how I felt about myself. They were, quite simply, embarrassing. They defined how I carried my body and how I stood and walked. I stooped over, hiding my chest—and my heart—at the same time. I developed a scrunched-shoulder posture I hold to this day, and I would imagine the same holds true for girls who develop early.

# Pancakes were my hugs and kisses

We never ate pancakes at breakfast. They were supper food and got me as excited as Matchbox cars did for some boys. I've heard that snorting cocaine feels like getting some very good news; that was me when I got wind that pancakes were for supper. But they came at a price.

Dad would turn silent three or four times a year. His episodes were less predictable than even the weather. They were like a dark cloud passed over the sun, and my heart would drop just a couple of inches in my chest. It was the same feeling as when my goldfish died.

Mom soothed my hurt feelings with her fluffy and perfectly round pancakes the size of a dinner plate. I needed their sweet and soft infusion so badly. A bite of a pancake was the closest thing I got to Disneyworld at the time; they were my happiest place on earth. They were a Nicotine patch I applied to get the good feelings and to smother the bad.

> **Food still works and is reliable as any drug. Sad? Confused? Worried? Hurt? A little dose of something sugary or creamy does the trick.**

The only problem is the whole addictive thing. Like I've heard it is with prescription painkillers (thank God, I've dodged those), you need more and more to get the same feeling. Plus, I swear you fry your own happiness genes when you continually flood your system with sweets; they do the happiness heavy lifting for you. Soon the fat starts to creep up on you, and then you begin to feel bad about that.

> **No one, I assert, feels better about themselves when they are fat.**

But for that night and many more, when my dad needed to check out from being my dad, the pancakes held me, patted my head, and told me I was okay. They let me know everything would be fine.

# The littlest (and most confused) food addict

I couldn't understand why I had to be the one who was fat? This was the 1970s; fat kids were the exception.

We went from kindergarten to senior year in one building, so everyone knew who the fat kids were, and there were only a few of us. I was a fatso and didn't understand how the fat lottery worked. At that age, I hadn't learned the whole fat cause and effect thing. The food going in and physical activity burning it off math problem was beyond me.

Food and eating were just a way of being in my family, and I was so immersed in my family, it's all I knew. I was cloistered among the cornfields, but I loved living in the old white farmhouse in the country, even with the extra pounds, and my dad who didn't seem to want to be my dad sometimes. Laying in the grass and watching the clouds pass, roaming the woods, and talking to the cows in the pasture—this is where I was happy. Alone in nature is where I felt safe to be myself.

I lived my days mimicking my funny and creative mom, my gentle father, and my sister, who I swear was a carbon copy of myself. They were my role models. What they did and said was my normal. I can't blame any of my life issues on them because despite whatever may surface on the page, I thought they were all rock stars, and I still do. I did what they did. Mom ate all the time and seemed to get happy from it. Dad sat in silent reflection for hours and he never denied his sadness. I hope his drinking and smoking helped him.

**Quite simply, fat runs in my family.**

There seems to be a gene passed down through the women on my mother's side beginning with Great Grandma Minnie and her size-13 feet that traveled southern Minnesota designing and sewing dresses for wealthy women. Then my grandma, Myrtle, matriarch of the family catering business, was a giant mound of a woman. She was bossy, smart, and cold to some, but I loved her so much. I could have lived in her apron pocket. In junior high, I wanted to move in with her and live in the giant hotel she also ran. Her life took off when her hard-living husband died, and her catering business grew to be famous in southern Minnesota. Weight issues didn't really extend to my aunts or uncles or on my dad's side, but my mom got it in spades from her mother, Myrtle. My sister got it from Mom, and maybe because I spent so much time with all these women, it rubbed off on me.

At the time, though, being fat seemed like a shitty luck of the draw. I sat and stewed in it. I thought maybe it was because I didn't clean up my toys or ate boogers like they were jellybeans. Maybe I was fat because I didn't pray and liked looking at the boys in the showers. I had the idea that if I did the PE calisthenics every day during summer vacation—the jumping jacks, burpees, and sit-ups—I would return to fifth grade just like the other kids. I'd be skinny and perfect and normal.

I knew what skinny and perfect looked like, thanks to the mail-order catalogs that landed in our mailbox. They were my window to the world. Sears was practical, JCPenney was the fanciest, and Montgomery Ward was the cheapest. We ordered clothes and toys on occasion, but they were mostly a book of dreams. In them, I saw who I dreamed of being and how I dreamed of looking. They were my Harlequin romance novels, and the hours I spent flipping through the pages kept me sane and hopeful. Sanity and hopefulness go well together. They were mail-order catalogs of who I wanted to be.

There was a model with blonde Peter Brady hair who looked like what I imagined a California boy to be. He would appear several times within the boy's section, though I couldn't fit into any of those clothes. Mom ordered my rectangular jeans from the men's section and cut them off; they would be so stiff when they arrived they could stand up by themselves. Everything else I wore she sewed or was a hand-me-down from my older sister.

This blonde boy was my ideal. He was slim and cocky in snow-white underwear and a smooth mound like a scoop of hard vanilla ice cream. He tucked his t-shirt into the elastic waistband that covered a flat stomach and pulled his tube socks with bold red stripes up to his knees.

On the next page, he was so perfect in navy blue gym shorts with white trim that scooped up the side of his legs, and a terry cloth tank top with stripes.

Confident people wear stripes. He was a PE warrior; I was the draft dodger who hid in the back. It was the spring/summer edition of the catalog and by the time I went back for fifth grade, I was somehow going to look just like catalog boy. I was about to rip his page out when my mom's voice bellowed, "Leave it be."

## Hello, first diet!

"So, how would you like to go to Weight Watchers?" Mom asked my sister and me like she read my mind, which I think she could. Did she somehow know I dreamed of being the skinny and cute catalog boy? She flicked the very long ash off her cigarette into the ashtray full of butts in the middle of the kitchen table. After long, empty stares from us both, she added, "We would all go."

But the idea came and went in a June afternoon, and I can imagine why. It was a small, small town and my poor mom and dad would get weighed in front of a bank teller and the pharmacist at the American Legion Hall. Plus, there was a rumor they sent you home with a picture of a pig to hang in your window if you gained weight, but that had to be a weight loss urban myth. Also, my dad really didn't have any weight to lose. His family didn't have the fat streak, and farmers work out all day long. Mom and Dad were always so beat by the time we finished milking cows at 8 p.m., were they really going to haul the seven miles into town to be told by a woman with a bouffant not to eat their feelings?

But, Mom was creative and a do-it-yourselfer. I mean, she made suitcases for us by covering cardboard beer cases with wood grain contact paper. She upholstered a couch in blue corduroy for my college dorm room and sewed a Disneyland-grade Mickey Mouse costume for me long after one should wear such a thing. Mom could make the fat family normal, all in a summer.

I could feel it was going to happen, and I was so excited. "No one's going to make fun of me anymore," I told Mom. She responded, "Well, you can't stop dumb people from doing the dumb things they're going to do, dear."

> **Still, I thought we would be like all the other families. Our car wouldn't sink when we all got in, and people wouldn't stare when the waitress brought our food at the Country Kitchen.**

There was always a brat in the next booth who'd say something like, "Look at all the food those fat people ordered." But now I would be like the boy in the JC Penney catalog hidden under my bed or inside my Mickey Mouse sleeping bag.

The *Better Homes and Gardens Low-Calorie Cookbook* was our diet Bible. I remember pudding with a skin on top with a dot of Cool Whip for dessert and pizza made on Rye Crisp crackers. Hamburgers cooked under the broiler to sizzle out the fat and served open-faced on half of an English muffin were my favorite. We ate a lot of cottage cheese. Weight Watchers chocolate soda (as bad as it sounds) and low-calorie Thousand Island dressing were in the fridge. I still can taste and smell the salad dressing when I think of that summer; it was a watery cross between the taste of mayonnaise and the smell of Bactine.

I laid around the living room and watched TV as I always did—TV was my everything—and I waited to get skinny like Richie Cunningham, Starsky and Hutch, and Lenny and Squiggy. I weighed myself every morning and watched for the needle to drop. It did at first, but then just camped out at 150, which was a fifteen-pound drop, but it didn't get me anywhere near the boy in the catalog.

It was the first of a long march of diets throughout my life. Because we got the *National Enquirer* delivered to our mailbox, I had a new one every week to dream about and to try, though I never did. I read them like I read the *Little House* series of books, but they showed me that losing weight was possible, at least for some people. I remember the Lady Di diet, where the writers tried to imagine what she ate, and each day ended with one fun-sized candy bar. It hadn't surfaced yet that she suffered terribly from bulimia. I'm sure, like me, one candy bar would turn into 30 for her.

A seed was planted: every day is a diet. Every day is the first day of my forthcoming skinny life. First, Mom's diet from *Better Homes and Gardens*, then my love of Richard Simmons in high school, then the fat free craze in my 20s, the South Beach diet in my 30s, and many weeks on the Cabbage Soup Diet carried me through the years. Maybe in some small way, they all contributed to my reaching 170 pounds. To this day, the Weight Watchers app lives on my phone, a nod to that first diet summer.

> **I wanted to feel as loved and popular as Richie Cunningham and as safe as the Brady Bunch kids. I wanted to feel these things while just being me, but the two didn't get along.**

When I let my insides out to play, I got looks and points and laughs and stares. People talked about me, and soon, they would hit and kick me. There was one awful kid who spat on my head and wiped his shoes on my pants, knowing full well I wouldn't do anything about it. Nobody loves a little fat boy, I thought, and certainly not a shy, femmy one.

Scared, awkward, and uncomfortable are what I remember feeling all the time. It was like my pants were constantly too short, and my shirt was too tight. I had holes in the toes of my sock, and my underwear rode up my crack. I felt like an awkward duck in a land full of hunters.

# Chapter 3

## Junior high: the two worst words in the world

Walking the hall to the junior high locker room, I could already feel it was going to be bad. My stomach, my everything inside, felt like it was eating itself. Nerves and panic and fear and dread went at me like the maggots on our dog who died that summer. My dog died, I was entering junior high, and the worst six years of my life were about to begin.

"Shit, look at that one," an eighth grader yelled, with a little Peter Brady squeak but mostly a changed voice, sounding like a man. "Did you get that belly from drinking beer?" I turned to stone and pretended I didn't hear. I became a statue; Mom had taught me how to do this. "Nah, you got a fat ass, too," he said. I did. I was a pre-teen pear.

Junior high boys are awful in general, but from talking with other formerly fat gay kids years later—there are a lot of us out there—that crew, at that time, at that place, was especially nasty. They were the worst of a street gang movie.

> I was stung by a wasp 20 years ago, and it still flares up and itches now and then. Things said to me in junior high do the same.

Leave me the fuck alone, is what I thought at the time, and fuck doesn't form easily in my mouth. It's like all the sugar has made it too sweet. Did the fat girls have it as bad? I bet they did.

Pretend you're not here, that you're invisible, I thought. But these were hunters, raised by hunters, and they liked a target and shit, what a quandary. I was an emu—odd looking and unable to fly. But emus can move quick, and I couldn't, so I was more of a penguin who waddled around the locker room.

The shower room was packed this one day, all fog and chatter, with every nozzle on every pole taken. All I could think to do was to try to cozy up to one of the other guys and reach over to get some of his water and what was I thinking? It was Jeff Someone, the biggest and meanest of the eighth graders. He had a big bush of pubic hair and looked like he was 25, so maybe I felt a little safe, like he was an adult, but he was all mean muscle and shoved me away so hard I hit the tiled wall, slid down, and landed on the floor looking up at 24 naked boys. I was turtle on his back.

"Get the fuck away from me you God-damned faggot." This cleared the room and just as I got myself up, this very short kid named Dave, a mean little leprechaun, performed a classic shower room stunt—a hard slap with both hands on the back that leaves red handprints that look like angel wings. But I sure didn't feel like any angels were on my back.

I gained about 30 pounds over the coming year. My adult mind tells me I needed the protection during this whole puberty/junior high/PE disaster. My 12-year-old self just needed the pain-relief.

I can still hear the sound of Mr. Klunder rolling out his big scale, like at the doctor's office, and then I walked up in front of everyone, and they all stood in silence. They were excited. You could almost smell it. They knew this was going to be good.

I stepped up and swayed a little on the metal square. He slid the bar over until it balanced, and like a BINGO caller, he yelled: 2–4–0. The class blew up like the explosion you hear when a crowd is watching football, cheering like I scored a surprise field goal. A loud "Geez" and a long "Whoa" mixed into one big roar through the echoey locker room.

I felt bad. Bad sums it up. Bad about myself. Bad about everything. Nothing else says it as well. Bad.

## Eating was my afterschool special

I never ate breakfast. I was too scared, too nervous about what my days were now like. I'd lay in bed as long as I could until Mom gave her last call: "Eric, you just have to get up." Like most of her sentences, it ended with an eruption into a smoker's cough that crackled.

I wouldn't eat lunch because I had to go into the cafeteria and wander lost to find someone who'd let me sit with them, of which there was no one. A school cafeteria isn't much different than those in prison movies and TV shows. To this day, the smell of hamburger hotdish makes me sad. Many years later, when poor Mom had landed in the nursing home and had to go down to the dining room, I could see how she dreaded it. She locked her jaw and stared blankly into the distance, much like I did in junior high. She'd wheel herself to the back of the room near the window, where she could stare outside like an animal in a cage.

That's how lunch time felt like every day for six years. My friend, James— my only friend— would race through the lunch line, shovel in his food, then he and I would walk to the drug store a block away, and he would buy a Snickers bar. I never got one. Eating alone was what gave me comfort. I just slumped along, and he walked silently with me, like a mute form of counseling.

He was fat, too, but not fat and a sissy, so he got off easier. "You know what they call us, don't you?" he asked. "Bosom buddies." I had suggested that maybe we shouldn't hang out together, to try to make it stop, but he objected. "We shouldn't let them get to us." He was a good and wise little friend—the only one I had for many years. I had stolen make-up from his mom a few years back when I had gone to his house to play, and Mom had found it. She questioned me about it, to which I just sat with my head hanging. I have no idea if his mom ever figured it out, so there was always a strained undercurrent between us, but he stood by me. The song, "Stand by Me," was written about people like him.

Every day, my sister and I got dropped off by the bus at the end of our farm's driveway. I walked slowly and about ten paces behind her up to the house, worn out and hungry for so much in life, food and otherwise. "How was your day?" Mom would ask, and she meant it. She really did care about her kids and how they were doing.

"Fine," I'd say with feigned cheeriness, and I'd head upstairs to change out of my school clothes. Back downstairs, I'd fill bowls and plates in the kitchen and carry them like a baby to the living room. A matted-down path in the striped wall-to-wall carpet ran from the kitchen to my chair next to the TV; it was incredibly like the path the cows wore in the pasture that led them to the barn at feeding and milking time.

Back in the kitchen, Mom smoked all over our food and watched *Match Game '77*. She seemed not to notice when I returned to hunt for more and more to fill the hole that was forming inside and developing an abscess. The soothing mushy comfort of several peanut butter sandwiches and many bowls of Cheerios soaked in sugar-laced milk became my everything.

They were my best friends, my only real friends, it seemed, except for Mom when I could catch her with the right mix of caffeine, nicotine, butter, and game shows in her system. My cereal bowl was the one we used for mashed potatoes at Thanksgiving. The sugar left at the bottom looked like sand on the beach, and I dragged my finger through it and drew little hearts and smiley faces.

The taste was never that important; it was all about the texture and the never-ending going down of it.

> **I couldn't get enough of the sweetness because I needed that so much in my life. I wanted it even more if it had a smooth, creamy texture. It felt like it held me.**

The new layers of fat were gradually forming like a long, slow snowfall. I was covering myself with first a sweater, then an afghan, then a blanket, then a sleeping bag zipped over my head to stay safe and warm.

# I hated myself... there, I said it

I don't remember the guy's name. It might have been Steve, a name I've hated my whole life, so it probably was. He and his family moved to town when we were in eighth grade, and that always made a kid a bit of a celebrity. I think we all got secretly bored with each other, and a new kid perked things up. Maybe that accounted for some of the aggression from all the boys. They were so bored in the cloistered little town, and they went at me like our chickens did to one another when cooped up all winter.

This Steve kid was new and different and he looked different. He was a city kid, and his parents opened a fancy supper club in the town a few miles down the road. This city kid was full-on mean, or at least mean to me. At first, I thought he had just caught on that this was the thing to do to fit in, though he was so perfect, did he really need it? His face looked like a grown-up, and his hair was exactly the way I wanted mine to be—a straight as an arrow part down the middle and feathered perfectly on the sides like a duck's wing. He was thin and played sports, and wore Levi's, and the little white tag on the back pocket of the corduroys was something I wanted so badly. But Levi's didn't go up to my size, and they were so expensive. Montgomery Ward had corduroys, cords as we called them, that went up to a 44-inch waist, but had no tag on the pocket, but I would cut a little one out of white fabric and tape it on.

When he snapped a rubber band at my face, he knew how to do it just right. He lifted it directly in front of me, pulled it back long and slow, and then held it like a gun in my face. That was the worst part; it was like getting shot at. And I wouldn't do a thing. I just sat there and maybe scrunched up my face a little as I dropped my head to the side and then muttered a little, "Don't." He laugh-mocked back, "Don't," as if to say, "Hey, look, all he does is say 'Don't.'" I didn't want to draw any attention to myself and what was happening to me. It was so embarrassing, and I was such a passive little thing and so scared of getting in a tussle. I certainly wasn't going to fight back.

The boys I grew up with who had turned on me and bullied and made fun of me upset me for sure, but they ultimately seemed to be doing it just for sport.

This guy was frightening. The rubber band gun was only his opening act.

The bell rang at the end of PE, and the whole crowd moved like an iceberg, and I hung back as I always did, and was always the last one to leave. I just wanted to be alone, and then like a car when it gets rear-ended, something splatted me against the wall. A thud against my back threw me forward and I turned. There was that mean grown-up face. A face that would kill someone in a movie. He knew what he was doing. He fought like a pro, and he pressed his arm against my neck, locking me against the wall, putting pressure on that very vulnerable part, the voice box, and maybe that's what locked my voice in my throat for so long. His knee pressed against my thigh, and he had that aggressive, chuckling look like a mean clown. "You piece of shit, you make me sick. You're a fucking joke, you gross faggot." Or it was very close to that. I have an excellent memory, and I specifically remember it sounded very adult, and he looked like one. What was most unsettling was that he did this in private, away from the crowd, with no one watching. It seemed personal. He wasn't showing off or trying to get along, like all the other boys seemed to be doing. He wanted to hurt me or even kill me. Then he punched me hard, straight into the gut, and I knew the feeling. It was like the time the tire swing boomeranged back and knocked the wind out of me. But I could take a hit like that and not double over or even flinch.

**Ignoring fags and fatsos trains you to ignore hits to the body, too.**

He attacked me a few more times, just to keep me guessing, and then a miracle happened. He left as quickly as he came. Sometimes trouble just goes away and finds some other poor soul to pester. He was like a tornado in the summer.

You wouldn't think all this stupid junior high shit would stick to the ribs and get caught in your teeth and hang around for a good chunk of your life, but for me, it did. My dad got kicked by a cow around this time and it gave him a forever trick knee. Junior high gave me an emotional trick knee that stuck around for at least 30 years.

*I hate myself. I hate my life.* I wrote it very small at the bottom of my workbook page, thinking someone, anyone might see it. Maybe God, but

I wanted Mr. Hislop, my gentle and kind English teacher, to read it and to do something. I wanted him to help me. I drew a box around it that started as four simple lines connected at the corners and then a tiny dot at the intersections with a circle around them. I continued to doodle small leaves to look like the ivy that Mom grew and wrapped around the curtains in the kitchen I loved so much. I dotted the ivy with several Spirograph-like flowers. I drew beautiful flowers, but no one seemed to notice.

## Could there be an easy way out?

I thought a lot about the kid from two towns over who hung himself with a sheet from the top bunk in his bedroom. We knew the family.

Most evenings I would hide in the barn to be by myself. The cows and the sheep seemed to be sad when they saw me, like they knew what I was going through. These barn animals were gentle-souled companions. Animals stare at us when we cry, and they seem to listen when we tell them our troubles.

I climbed the ladder up to the hayloft and stripped down to nothing. I took my rolls of fat and squeezed them and pushed them and pressed at them and slapped them, to try to break up the cells. I hoped this would release them from my body and I would go back to the house and leave them in the toilet.

Ropes hung everywhere in the hayloft, like the vines on *Gilligan's Island*. I'd twirl them, and they spun circles like the ropes in PE class when the skinny kids would climb up and touch the ceiling. The rhythm hypnotized me.

The hayloft seemed like the perfect place to exit, to disappear, to just remove myself from life. I could so easily and casually slip a rope around my neck, not even noose-style, but more like a jauntily tied scarf—and jump. I was sure it would appear to be an accident or a silly stunt gone wrong. There were mounds of slippery straw and hay piled all around, quite precarious to maneuver over. I had such a theatrical way about me, a freak accident was bound to happen. I fantasized about this so many days, but I could never get anywhere near the point of doing it.

24

> **I felt gutless, but maybe I was surrounded by angels who were busting their asses to keep me around until things picked up a few years later.**

I woke up on Saturday mornings feeling great, like the morning you wake up and realize your cold is gone. Suddenly you can breathe, and your throat isn't sore. I still had a streak of optimism in me. I tried to imagine an incredibly confident little Eric busting through the skin of the scared shitless one who traveled the halls of school afraid and on guard for the next horrible thing to happen. I pictured my imaginary superhero Eric. He would not give a damn and would refuse to go to PE class and would yell and fight back and get in trouble and not care about getting hauled into the principal's office because he would use the self-defense plea. He would make himself so strange and crazy that no one would have given him an ounce of shit. *They* would have been scared shitless, not him.

This is the adult me dreaming of how I could have handled the situation. The 13-year-old Eric was simply in hell.

## My free zone where I could be myself...we all have one

The gym was dark. The only lights were shining on the 1980s cover band hired to play the high school dance. I tried to look as casual as possible, leaning against the wall as the kids in my class walked by me like I was one of the decorations. The whole affair seemed like one of those scenes in a movie when everything is wavy and distorted from the main character's point of view. From somewhere, I found the guts to dance by myself. I simply had to, and it just started to happen, as easily as compulsive eating. "You look like you don't even know you're eating," Mom once told me. That's how easy dancing felt.

I was somehow invisible on the dance floor like it was a magical free space. I could dance near the other kids, but I was by myself. I was also dancing with the lead singer with the big hair like a Restoration wig and black lycra body suit displaying an enormous pouch of genitalia, as the spotlight seemed to focus on his bag of marbles. "Carry On Wayward Son" pounded through the tinny speakers and bounced off the cement block walls of the gym, and then passed through my body like radiation, and I was free. I was oddly safe. I felt like someone, not a garbage can or punching bag.

I could feel the cells of my body. When I danced, I felt at home in my skin (the dream of every fat person), and I grew weightless. The many extra pounds, 100 or so, were not fat, but tulle wrapped in layers around me that lifted me higher as I began to soar through the air. The thumping beat synced with my heart, and my body pulsed along with the drummer as he stepped down in rhythm on the foot pedal of the bass drum. The lead singer's power anthem voice filled me like a helium balloon.

I wasn't dancing with my body; I was dancing with my soul that could have been at Studio 54, which was open at the time in New York over 1,000 miles away. I was in the feet of Gene Kelly; I was the penny in his loafers that tapped manly in *An American in Paris*. I was a showgirl in Las Vegas, topless, and so proud of my drop-dead knockers that were huge, yet buoyant. Giant peacock feathers sprouted from my head.

I couldn't find my way or fit into this weird junior high world ruled by some sort of code I couldn't crack. I didn't even have a pencil and paper to try to figure it out. But I could dance. Like singing, I believe you're either a dancer or you're not.

> **Something is truly a part of you when you don't give a damn what others are thinking or saying or yelling or chanting when you do it. It's the stuff of fantasies for a fat person.**

It's the vanishing of the dimply goo and awkwardness. Like a magic trick, the fat disappears.

No one else in Arlington had the dance inside them like me. They posed and pretended in fake sideways spasms. My dancing sprung out of a seed deep inside that connected to all that was beautiful and interesting and also weird in the world. It was lifesaving. Dancing saved me.

I danced until 9:30 when Mom picked me up, and she likely asked me why I was so out of breath and sweaty. I'm sure I lied and told her that I was dancing with all my friends when what I was really doing was having as close to sex as I would have for a long time.

Soon I couldn't even go to school dances because the laughing and pointing and whispers won out. My K-Tel records at home on my little plastic turntable became my lifeline. They were my air hose to something higher. It was my only connection to God, who supposedly was a "savior."

## Are you there, God? It's me, Fatso.

Maybe things would have changed if I had tried to be a bible banger and pray for the mean boys who attacked me. I could have stood out on the football field with the giant lights turned on me and raised my palms to the sky and screamed "Holy Moly" to God like an evangelical. I could have just accepted God's mission to suffer through. When I got slapped, I could have turned the other cheek, but instead I cried and felt all alone, and in a small way, stoned and crucified. I felt like the town's sacrifice to God. How could I have sat through a dozen years of Sunday School without so much as a whisper that someone up there was taking care of me? If only I could eat and eat and not get fat, now that would be a God I could get behind.

So, help was not sent from above, and I didn't get the security from Mom and Dad that probably rarely happens anyway. I fantasized about parents who would hold me and tell me everything would be okay. They would home-school me because there was no way this Arlington school would ever work for a sissy, 260-pounder with feathered hair and pretty features so delicate that many thought he was a girl. It was the 1970s and 80s. This was a tall order for parents at the time.

> **The truth is, I was being damaged to the point it would take 20 years to make peace with it.**

## I found God in a tube of Townhouse crackers

Townhouse crackers stack so well and a whole tube could disappear and no one noticed. Or so I imagined. I would slide the sleeve out of the box and head upstairs. I'd sit on the edge of my bed and stare into the hall and out the window that faced the west as the sun came down. I could tear open the tube of crackers and eat them as if I was keeping time with my heartbeat as I stared at the orange sky. The crunch snapped me out of my daze, and a jolt from the salt pulled me out of my depression for a second. It seemed to work like Carrie Fischer said electro-shock helped her. It dulled the thinking like Francis Farmer's lobotomy.

I would hear the screen door slam like a gavel. I'd watch out the window to see Mom head out to her garden to cut chives to put in the sour cream for our supper baked potatoes. I'd sneak down the stairs like a 260-pound ballet dancer, though there was no real reason to be quiet. I'd find my way into the giant pile of goodies on the counter next to the fridge.

I would take at least five doughnuts from the variety pack; it was the same pack of goodness I ate when I was four. Back then, I loved the powdered sugar one, but now it was too much tell-tale dust on my face, so I went for the chocolate and the crunchy ones. I would slide into my secret chair in the back of the dining room, behind a pile of fabric the size of a haystack, and next to our collection of *World Book* encyclopedias. Maybe I would read about sunny Spain, so far away. The soft, cozy doughnuts shot doses of calm and pleasure into me. They were little life preservers. If Mom was gone long enough, I could get to the fridge, open the mayonnaise, and begin a rapid fire of tablespoons of the stiff, creamy, eggy goo into me.

> **Each spoon seemed to send me farther away from my heart, where things didn't hurt so much.**

## Chocolate Delicious dessert: My drug of choice

I climbed down the stairs from the wrestling room above the pool, sore as hell from lumpy somersaults across the mat in PE. Out of nowhere, Jerome showed up.

The stairwell was all cement blocks and steel, like the set of the infamous prison episode of *Charlie's Angels,* where the girls went undercover. I had grown pretty sharp at maneuvering myself around danger, but Jerome usually wasn't one of my worries. He could be nice, but he also reminded me of the type of guy who'd put razor blades in apples for trick-or-treaters. He jumped down the stairs behind me, three at a time. I assumed he'd just do his usual and call me a fat-ass as he flew by and tell me to hurry up, but his outstretched arm smacked my back right in the middle, and my head jerked back. I was a crash test dummy in a TV commercial.

I could be graceful, even at 280 pounds, and I kept myself upright as I grabbed the handrail and took the next three stairs in one step and the next three in another as the world twirled around me. I spun and collapsed into the final step, and my shin bone cracked against it as I landed face down on the cement with what looked like little stones embedded in it.

For a minute, I wasn't sure where I was, but I wished I was anywhere but in a stairwell in a school in a town that truthfully bored me and I hated.

But I had seen enough after-school specials about bullying to know to just get myself up, which I did. I grabbed the end of the railing with one hand and the rough cement wall with the other. But I couldn't walk. I stepped on my foot, and my leg didn't work. I was the little clown toy I had at home that when you pressed the button on the bottom, he collapsed.

So, I stood there and tried what I had heard in church all those years. I prayed for help. Real hard and very serious, like "God, I'm not messing around here anymore. Get to work!"

And in a couple of minutes, I could step on my leg. Maybe that's how long it takes for a prayer to get up there and then find me again in the cement block confines of the pool/weight room/locker room bunker that smelled like dust, rubber, and sweat. I walked like a car with one flat tire. The school bell had rung, the period was over, and all the other boys had stripped, showered, dressed and left, along with Mr. Klunder, the teacher. I dressed slowly, the way my mom had to when she was 80.

That was one of the many days I remember going home and sulking.

**About 75% of my evenings and weekends, I sat in a haze of sadness.**

I was such a good boy; I never snuck beer from my dad's kegerator in the garage, but honestly, who could have blamed me? The buzz would have been such a relief but I'm sure I would have quickly slipped down the booze rabbit hole.

Our house didn't have any good pills in the medicine cabinet, but my oxycontin was a whole pan of chocolate delicious dessert, as we called it at my grandma's catering company. It was a cake pan filled with a crust of butter, sugar, and flour, and sequential layers of Cool Whip, chocolate pudding, cream cheese, and a shaved chocolate bar on top. The whole affair resembled the plowed Minnesota farm fields in the winter. When snow blows over the ground, it catches in the long drifts of frozen overturned soil, and the peaks of black stick up through the white, looking like a scantily frosted devil's food cake.

There were so many of these desserts made at Grandma's and the extras always made it to our house. They were so smooth and easy to eat, nearly melting into a soothing liquid form, and I basically shot them into my arm. A pan of chocolate dessert was a ten-minute ride that stopped racing thoughts of hurt. It was the closest thing to feeling normal that I could find.

> Questioning everything about myself was fast becoming my constant pastime. Food choked off the parts I deemed wrong and the ones that hurt from being vulnerable and exposed. The more food I could get into myself, the more the awful feelings were smothered.

## Hurt people hurt goats

Our giant goat, Winston, was named after the cigarettes my mom smoked. He was pesky and always needed to be in the middle of things and he ate our petunias and snapdragons and climbed on the roof of the car like a monkey in a tree. But he was no more obnoxiously goat-like than the average goat. We had to castrate him by putting a rubber band around his little sack. A week later it fell off, and I found it and kept it. It was like a little goat coin purse.

The poor old guy would be so happy to see me when I came home from school, and we would head out to the backyard and the barn to play. It was an escape for me and a celebration for him. We had so many great boy/goat moments. I would brush his wiry white coat until it was fluffy, walk the field roads and roam the woods with him by my side, his head cocked up at me; his glassy green eyes looked like a horizontal keyhole at the center. He always had a little smirk on his face, a constant half-smile. He spoke with his Billy goat bleat like a tinny phone ringing.

It had been a bad day at school, the particulars I don't recall, but I was playing on the jungle gym dad had welded together. It was a masterpiece, really, and on it I hung like a depressed orangutan.

Winston came out of nowhere and knocked me off my perch. Perhaps I had just had my fill that day, and I picked up the trapeze pole, a three-foot-long piece of pipe with long chains at either end, and swung it across his enormous belly. Hard. Very, very hard. It made a deep thud like a bass drum, and he stumbled backward, his hind legs giving out, and he fell to the ground like he had been shot.

I screamed at him, a guttural and ugly, "I hate you, you stupid, fucking, big fat old goat," or something very close to it. I went at him and grabbed his horns and twisted his neck like I wanted to break it.

Something about the way he looked at me, like he was hurt and confused, and perhaps like he could see what was going on inside, switched all my anger to sadness, and I dropped to the ground with him. We both sat in a sad pile.

Goats are very resilient. They eat pop cans. He also had his bad days when he would charge at me and butt me in the gut so hard it knocked the wind out. But that's different. He was playing. I was just plain old mean. No better than the boys at school, and it makes me think of what they might have been going through at home. I know for sure at least one of them was pretty severely abused.

This was the cruelest I've ever been to any being in my life, and to write about it makes me as sad as I've been in a long time. My heart breaks. And my hands cradle my head—literally.

I don't remember the day Winston died, but I remember Dad found him outside the barn, and he had been dead long enough for his body to bloat so that his legs lifted up to the sky.

Will it ease my guilt if I write, "I'm so sorry, Winston!" fifty times on a sheet of notebook paper? When I die, I will seek him out first, in the back pastures of heaven, and make it up to him by brushing his fur for hours and polishing his horns like marble.

Winston, maybe you felt loved and well-cared for and special. Perhaps that day we brought you home, a little goat the size of a cocker spaniel, with your little bleat that sounded only like fanning a deck of cards, maybe, oh maybe that was the start of what was a beautiful life that you loved every minute of.

I guess hurt people really do hurt people. And goats.

# Chapter 4

## Could Richard Simmons save me?

TV was my direct link to something, anything out in the world that might save me. Who happened to show up 12 inches tall on it one day but Richard Simmons, the frantic little frizzy-headed God of the obese. Could he be my savior?

During his 30-minute show, Richard cooked, exercised, and interviewed fat women, and I would watch slouched in my favorite big brown chair like a fat cat, pulled up as close to the TV as possible. It was a soap opera to me. I wasn't as interested in what he said as I was in the drama of him. It's not that I wasn't intrigued by his words, I was just so smothered in the fat and dependent on the compulsive eating and the escape and the relief it gave me, I didn't believe that any of this could ever work for me.

But Richard, he mesmerized. He was enormous, then got skinny; now he was even fit and had muscles. And he was gay as Christmas. I was nearly 300 pounds and also flamboyant as a headdress. I was him when he was younger.

He could be himself and he made his way in the world just fine. He was more than fine; he grew rich and famous and he was a TV star. People thought he was really something. I never tried his Deal-A-Meal cards or Sweatin' to the Oldies videos, but I did read his *Never Say Diet* book (diet has the word die in it) and then the companion cookbook, over and over like a prayer book.

On the lonely winter plains of southern Minnesota in the 80s, posters of Jon Bon Jovi and Ted Nugent and girls holding their boobs were what hung on most teen boy's bedroom walls; above my desk hung the detailed lead pencil sketch I drew of Richard in art class. I worked intently to capture every crazy hair in his puffball, the many folds in his tracksuit, and the overt smile causing many wrinkles on his face like I would have decades later. He held a bright, smiley, and rather empty expression.

I sent off for one of the t-shirts advertised at the end of the show. It had *The Richard Simmons Show* printed across the chest, but it should have read: *Beware, don't meet your heroes*, because ten years later, I did. He stopped at the Eden Prairie Mall on one of his promotional fat tours in the 90s, and I made a pilgrimage to see him. There I was with several hundred women and about ten men; it was like a rock concert mixed with a spiritual revival. Did I subconsciously wear my hot pink t-shirt so he'd pull me out of the crowd? If I did, it worked.

It was a segment just for the guys, and six of us were hand-picked by him. I had to make a giant step up to the stage, every big person's nightmare, but there was no judgment in this crowd as my enormous rear-end the size of a tractor seat pointed towards them. I think a couple of soul sisters even helped me up. Maybe the ladies saw I was wearing women's pants from Fashion Bug Plus.

Richard gathered us into a huddle, and none of the others were big guys or even had the look of ever being one. They were obvious tag-a-long husbands. All were straight men, my nemesis, the source of all my fear in the world, and Richard acted like he was one of them.

"OK, men," he said in the huddle, and he wasn't even looking at me, just glossing over my hopeful eyes. "Imagine that there are 500 horny women out there." *What the hell?* Then he screamed at the audience, "OK, ladies, let these hunks know you want to see their best sexy man dance moves. Are you ready, men?"

I worked my way to the back of the stage, shrinking like a dog does when it's discovered he tore up the garbage. There I stood, like a toy with dying batteries.

Richard, damn you, this was supposed to be a safe space. A place for you and me to connect.

Richard wasn't my weight loss guru. No one ever turned out to be, and I don't think anybody turns out to be for anyone. We can only do that for ourselves, but more on that later.

**Oh, what if I could have somehow given myself the love and affirmation I was looking for from him?**

If only I could have mustered up the confidence, the wherewithal he must have had to become Richard Simmons. Our meeting that night in the Eden Prairie Mall helped me see that no one could do anything about this but myself.

But maybe reading his book helped. To this day, I think the only thing that really makes a difference is to hear how others did it.

It seemed I was beginning to hate school and life a little less. After four years of being the constant butt of cruel and very homophobic jokes, I either got used to it, or all the bullies grew bored with pestering me. I could still see their shenanigans out of the corner of my eye, but I no longer felt like I was being followed by a hit squad of sorts. This opened up some real estate in my psyche, and adult thoughts seemed to be crowding out my helpless, childlike ones.

I was 16, and a strong, strong desire to get skinny overcame me. A glimmer of hope that I could actually do it also appeared—this was the part that was especially new and different. Up until this point, I just hated being fat, and I hated the way people treated me for being fat, but I had no clue how to change any of it because food was all I had.

**Maybe all the generalized hate and frustration collided with developing hormones because it was the first time it clicked that I could actually lose weight.**

I so wanted to be thin and I wanted to not stick out like a sore thumb. Maybe all this, with a little Richard sprinkled in, started to turn the car around for me.

My sad grades lifted, and I was on the A honor roll throughout my junior and senior years. I was lucky to have a world-class English and Drama teacher. Theater and writing became my emotional release. Along with eating, they were my salvation.

Mr. Moore's classes remain to this day, the most profound learning experiences I've had, including seven years of college. He assigned us to keep a journal, and it was a turning point. We were to write a page a day. I averaged at least five. Out poured frustration, fear, humiliation, shame, anger, and rage, but also hopes and dreams. Journaling to sort through my thoughts and to get the bad juju out has remained a constant in my life, mainly because it works.

At the same time, an Intro. to Psychology class was like cracking open the book of life. Outside of my writing (and art classes), it was the first time school had any point. How could a class that had something to do with feelings and emotions exist in my high school? History class, which at the time was all politics, was like reading the phone book. Algebra and geometry were migraine headaches. This lit me up.

We covered the three body types: ecto-, endo- and mesomorph. I thought I was the last one because Mr. Rewerts gave Santa Claus as the example, but I eventually discovered I was more a bony ecto underneath. Freud's theory of the id, ego, and superego, and how we all have three people inside, is what I remember the most. I'm not alone in having what feels like several people living inside me, I thought. My id wishes death on the boys in my class. My superego shames me for my bad thoughts and actions, and my ego tries to make peace with the two by eating. Or maybe it was my id that consumed food like a tornado. This is all a simplification, but it's how my teen boy brain processed it. It was a flicker of self-awareness.

I also remember the theory of the shadow and how we all have these dark sides we ignore because they seem too awful to face. What I may have been doing is facing my shadow in my writing. Of course, none of this was clear at the time, but it was a glimmer of hope in a grizzly period of life.

At 16, I could lose five pounds in a week. Most teen boys can, especially those staring 300 pounds in the face.

If I ate only one plate of whatever Mom cooked for supper—even a round pile of Salisbury steak on a bed of buttered noodles—I would weigh less the next morning. Many nights I began to walk the gravel roads around the farm. It was initially to just get out of the house and be alone with the hurricane of thoughts and emotions inside me, but it grew to be life-changing.

The temperature and humidity are often high in July and August in Minnesota. The air is thick, and the sun slides to the horizon through a sort of gauze as the crickets chirp in the background. It was like walking in a terrarium, but I recall I loved the sweat that poured off me. I felt like I was sweating out the generalized bad craziness inside. I didn't care that I was a big and wet mess, which is how I usually felt anytime, anywhere, out in public.

If it was especially hot and humid, I'd ride my bike for an hour, but not very far. I'd bike a mile and then back, and then a mile the other direction, and then back, and so on. I was weightless on my bike. I felt like I was 165 pounds.

Those nights on the farm were magical; I was discovering I could make a change in myself. As I biked, I met so many dragonflies that would ride along with me as if they had something they wanted to say. Their big alien-like eyes told me that this was what I needed—to get up and get out in the thick evening air. Dragonflies can make one feel like everything is going to be okay.

Those were the good nights. Many others were like I'd been shot by a tranquilizer gun and I'd land in my big chair for a night of eating and TV. I needed to be someone else, somewhere other than the farm on many nights. It might have been part lazy teen, but my perennial sadness seemed to have ripened into a type of depression. Also, I think overwhelm and laziness get confused with each other.

Laziness and depression have always been on either end of a teeter-totter in me, and they challenge each other to see who's in charge. I've had periods of depression throughout my life, and I'm lucky in that the bouts can usually be tied to something circumstantial that's going on. High school is a perfect example of this.

In adulthood, I can remove myself from situations that depress me like bitchy workplaces, houses in bad neighborhoods, and relatives that are nasty. At 16, I couldn't do that. To this day, when I get the more garden-variety blues for a spell, action of some sort, any sort, always helps. Maybe the walking and biking at night was shaking loose the depression or blues or plain-old sadness and sorting through the overwhelm.

## Fat was a family loyalty

I had good days, but nothing could break me from my emotional eating.

> **If I tried to eat less, I felt this odd sense of betrayal, like I rejected a second helping of Mom's love and affection, though she never came out and said it.**

She and I were linked though; we had set up a communication system in the womb. A chip had been implanted in me, and I could sense what she felt, thought, needed, and wanted.

For so many years, and sometimes to this day, I feel the same kind of pull. When I try to move forward and release old thoughts, habits, and rancid thinking, I get snapped back, like an emotional rubber band is tied to my back. I hold an allegiance to something in my past. Eating in my chair in the living room, watching TV, and going back to the kitchen ten times a night, still feels loyal to my family.

## I swallowed everything

It was my last year of PE, and the public weigh-in spectacle would finally end. By this age, it was more like a prison yard in a movie as I stepped on the scale. Voices mumbled as the guys, many with mullets, spoke low to one another, then craned their necks to see. But I showed them. I wasn't 300 pounds. I just skimmed under at 297, and now I was so good at making myself invisible. It was now my superpower. I would disconnect and transfer my feelings from my heart into my gut. They would be buried deep in there, and my big belly could take the hits and protect me. Folding into myself was the best way to get by in life.

The bigger I grew, the further away from myself I became. I continued to build one of the sandbag walls that towns assemble when spring floods come. I filled sacks full of giggles I saw out of the corner of my eye and the looks and mumbles of all the boys in school.

Nothing was dependable or safe, and all I could do to make sense of it was to conclude it was something I did or didn't do, who I was or wasn't. I felt like a big disappointment to everyone in my world. What did I do with these emotions like mosquitoes that bit and buzzed in my ears? I ate them. Eating was a sure thing. It was so dependable.

> **I continued to swallow everything. My feelings that didn't taste very good, along with any food I could get my hands on.**

But then again, taste has so little to do with compulsive, emotional eating. Tasteless or mild food is better because you're just cramming it in and wasting it when the kids on the commercials are starving and bloating on the other side of the world. Bland seems like less of a waste and less pure indulgence. Somehow, it's not even food you're stuffing in you, but more like an anonymous substance. Spicy and delicious get in the way. They slow it down and ignite the flame inside and stir emotions more.

Mashed potatoes and white cake with frosting (wedding cake is perfect) and plain old vanilla ice cream are the best. They are the white foam that sprays from a fire extinguisher. The thick wool blanket that smothers a fire. When these white foods were near, and no one was around, I'd get as excited as I imagine most kids my age were getting about making out. I would get a food erection.

A giant metal tub of vanilla ice cream was always wedged in our freezer the size of a VW Beetle. I would first wrestle the faux wood salad bowl the size of a hard hat out of the stack of bowls in the cupboard. With a serving spoon the size of a garden trowel, I'd work enormous curls off the hard block of sugar and cream. I'd scrape until I had a bowl of ribbons and then twirl the whole mass around until it began to melt and turn into a creamy vortex that was not so much eaten but inserted. I took it in, and it soothed all the crazy and sad thoughts, and guilty feelings. What was all the guilt and shame about? Details would eventually be made clear, but at the time, it was just a general feeling like everything about me was wrong. Vague guilt and shame are constant pains. They're like having a sore seat, as my mom put it, after a bout of diarrhea.

> **The sugar kicked in, and I felt like I was the Homecoming King of my own little world for a while. I could get whatever I wanted and be whomever I wanted to be.**

I would walk into the gym, and people would wave at me and cheer and chant my name, and I climbed up on the stage and waved back cocky as hell. There I would stay until the bowl was gone and licked clean like I was a dog.

A daze would set in, and I'd fall asleep. Thirty minutes later, I'd wake up to *One Day at A Time* and stare at Valerie Bertinelli; how perfect life must be when you're that cute and sassy with always a snappy comeback and the whole world is in love with you.

I soon found out I was lucky, and because of an allergy or some kind of dairy intolerance, with a little tightening of my gut, avalanches of ice cream would come flying up. I'd walk down the driveway away from the farm and leave it in the tall weeds that lined the road. So, the bad thoughts I made worse by eating like a disgusting pig were gone; I exorcised the demons. Suddenly I felt repented and light as air. My body puked on its own. I didn't even need to stick my finger down my throat, which could sound like I had just won the lottery, but stay tuned.

# The high school speech I wanted to give

My high school speech career was dismal. All I wanted was the validation of trophies and ribbons, but I think I was a little too melodramatic for most judge's palates. I was raised on *Dallas* and *One Life to Live*. Alexis Carrington was my speech role model. But what if I had really spoken from the gut? If only I could have given the speech that was inside me somewhere but sealed inside a little shellacked paper mâché heart of what I was supposed to think, feel, and speak.

It might have gone like this: "You know, this is all such bullshit, and it just sucks," I would have said. "I am just so fucking miserable I can't take it anymore. I know I'm a freak; I'm just so different than all of you. And yeah, it seems like I try to be like you, but there are moments when I'm all alone, likely outside, somewhere on the farm, sitting in a tree which always fills me with common sense, and I know I don't want any of this B.S. I guess it's not your fault, all you high school shitheads. I just landed in the wrong place at the wrong time, and maybe I'm a peace-loving soul who didn't have the fight in me. I don't give a damn, this is who I am, and you can punch me and slap me and laugh at me and push me as I walk down the hall and snap rubber bands at my back and wipe your shoes on me and spit on my head and punch me like you're attempting to deflate me. It just doesn't matter, and I will forge ahead with all the things I love and study hard and get excellent grades and rehearse my speeches and memorize my lines and practice my saxophone and challenge the bitches up to first chair and star at state. I'll dress in cherry red corduroys and pink and purple sweaters, wear necklaces, rings, hats, and carry notebooks and folders with flowers. I will be so confident and sink my teeth into everything I love when I am home at night and on the weekends, and I won't eat wildly and mindlessly like a starving dog. I'll become thin and trim and rather handsome, and I will be set on my path in life and not be poised to suffer a sort of arrested development for at least another 20 years because the truth is, all I want is to be happy and get along with people. In the end, I still like people, in spite of you all."

That's what I could have said. Maybe if I had, it would have been the speech that won the first-place trophy I wanted so badly, but never got.

## The scale was my bad high school boyfriend

I would sneak, and I mean literally sneak down the path through the backyard to the barn. Like in a 1940s movie, I'd look back over my shoulder to make sure no one was around as I pulled open the door the size of a billboard. There sat the old feed scale. I looked back up to the house to make sure I wasn't followed, and I stepped into the cold milk room with cement floors and cinder block walls. I pulled off my sweatshirt the size of a Mumu, tossed it on the empty milk tank, and dropped my sweats like clown pants over the drain in the floor. I slid off my red underwear with orange trim and stepped onto the platform to see where I was at.

If I had been good the day before and the scale showed it, I was ecstatic, but even if I lost a couple of pounds, the high was so short-lived. In a few hours, I would sink back to the idea that I weighed twice as much as most of the boys in my class, but they had snuff to chew on, pot to smoke, and chicks to bang to feel better. I didn't even masturbate. I couldn't figure it out and had no one to explain it to me. Who was I going to pick it up from? The barn cat who rubbed her puffy crotch on the fence?

**Touching myself down there made me feel even more of a bad boy than I already felt I was. The scale was my boyfriend. I dated food.**

If I had pigged out the night before (there is just no better term) and the scale hadn't gone up, I felt lucky. If the arm flew up and indicated the weights were too light, I sank, like someone sliced through the Bozo punching bag clown with a pen knife. I would scream low and hard, but my screams and my words and my singing and my laughs always caught in my throat, so instead I slapped my big, gelatinous gut.

# The graduate had a high score of 320

It was prom time, the high school ritual dreaded by those of us who don't fit in. At least I could try to have some fun with what I wore. I had fantasized a burgundy corduroy ensemble with a pink shirt and a wild print tie, maybe daisies or paisley or even a flamingo. Dad and I drove to the Twin Cities to find one. We walked into Jerry Leonard's Big and Tall Men's store in the mall that smelled like Cinnabon and told the big and tall man with the Coke bottle glasses that we needed a suit for prom. I was excited, but he looked me up and down and showed me the one suit that would fit me. It was a horrible gray, the color of galvanized steel, with a vest that reversed to a faint blue plaid, like the grid notebooks we used in science class. The pattern was the one bit of flair to the yards and yards of polyester. I was even too big to get a cool suit in a joint like that.

The suit could have stood up by itself; I looked and moved like the Tinman in *The Wizard of Oz*. The little boutonniere I made myself was tiny on my enormous gray wall of a body; it was a flower poking out of a crack in a retaining wall. The suit was stiff, slippery, and cold, but I was over 300 pounds by this time, so the feel of it was a relief. I would sweat anytime I had to move at all, and certainly when I was in front of a group of people, or someone looked at me like I was horse poop on a parade route. My right armpit drips when I think I'm in trouble or have done something wrong, and it was wet all the time because I felt that everything about me was wrong and could get me in trouble. I actually sweated through the jacket of the suit.

> There was a certain strange satisfaction ending high school at 320 pounds. By getting bigger, I said to everyone: "You can make all the fun of me you want, I don't give a damn. I am fat, and I will keep getting fatter, so I won, or at least you didn't win. You didn't get under my skin enough to make me change."

Yeah, I ended up sort of average in high school in so many ways. I was too sad and weighed down to engage in anything, but I succeeded in getting as big as I could. The thing I loved to do the most, this is what I excelled at. I won—320 pounds at graduation. I was the valedictorian of fat.

The only thing graduation was to me was the end of putting in my time and suffering through six years of a type of prison. The diploma felt like a certificate of, "Yeah, well, I really fucked up and pissed this all away, and I just feel so mediocre about it." But what was I supposed to do? I was miserable. Ironically, I had just been voted "Most Optimistic," but it was a pity designation. I tied with someone else, and they likely felt bad for me, and wanted everyone to get something. Everyone needed a trophy. Or everyone mistook my plastered-on grin for optimism. It was a smile mask that covered fear and sadness.

The graduation gown was perfect. It skimmed over everything bad and shameful, and no one saw the huge, silly boy walk in. I was terrified as I waited to cross the stage. What was going to get yelled out from the crowd? I sensed something was going to happen. I could already hear the "Fag. Queer. Fatso. Sissy. Loser." Oh, God, please don't let anyone yell anything as I walk in front of everyone at 320 pounds in what looked like a kaftan.

I would be outed as a complete nothing, but at least I was done with all the hell. I made it halfway across the stage, and the school board president extended his hand.

No one yelled, but they didn't need to. I heard it all, anyway.

**Somehow, I was going to be thin one day. I just knew it. No matter what it took, I was going to be skinny.**


## Lost in a cornfield

I was a gay, fat farm kid from southern Minnesota who hadn't been beyond the upper Midwest. I saw the world like I saw Arlington, and it's amazing how terrified I was of a town the size of most graduating classes. The world seemed fickle and mean. It was one big bully. The only way for me to survive was to present myself in a way that would not get me picked on (or killed), but there comes a time when the veneer cracks.

It was after one of the giant weddings we catered with my grandma. I hated weddings because they seemed like a club I could never join, though I still was telling myself I could find a girl to marry. The church basement kitchen was piled full of giant kettles and pans of baked-on food that first needed to be soaked, and then scoured in nearly boiling water and bleach. The 500 plates were loaded into the sink and washed one by one, which was my job. The older lady workers packed away leftover food, and I looked around, and everything inside me looked and felt like these piles of dirty dishes. Out in the dining room, "they" were laughing and pointing at the 300-plus pound boy/man. An hour earlier, one southern Minnesota dude had thought he was hilarious when I refilled the bowl of mashed potatoes the size of a kitchen sink. "Hey, big fellow, the food sure must be good." Then he looked at his buddies, and they all explosion-laughed like drunk men do. Maybe they were all so wasted they didn't notice the stream of sweat running down and off my face that dripped into the bowl of potatoes they ate. These big, drunk guys ate a part of me.

Graduation had been a month ago, and now my future made me feel like my veins were running with the gravy we served that was thickened with flour. I felt like I was wrapped like a mummy in one of the five-foot-wide and endless rolls of paper tablecloths we used to cover the banquet tables. I took one of these rolls out to the van to begin loading for the way home, but I crawled into the front seat and held the roll. All I could do was gently stroke the paper and focus on the texture and the gentle scraping sound. I was having one of those old-fashioned nervous breakdowns that we heard women have in the Twin Cities. My aunt had one, Mom told me later. She and her other sister walked her around the Southdale Mall to help her get back on her emotional feet.

I sat in the van feeling like the painting of the condemned sinner. I was so scared of everything.

Mom came out the back door and looked at me in the front seat like "What the hell is going on?" was playing in her mind. When she came around

45

to the door, all I could think to tell her was, "I think I'm having a nervous breakdown."

"Oh, no, Eric," she said. She responded the way she had when the vet told us our collie had cancer. Her words were filled with softness and warmth and a little dread mixed in, like she had been waiting for this. Mom saw everything that went down with me, though she never said a word. She also knew that things like this ran in our family. There was my aunt's nervous breakdown, but the real clincher was my dad's two brothers who had taken their own lives. I'm sure she feared her own moody husband was on the brink of doing it as well, and now her son was spiraling around the drain.

She sat with me in the van, but I can't remember the conversation. I'm sure what I said was a sideways dance around feeling terrified of everything and like I didn't fit in anywhere. I felt everyone's first reaction to me was that I was so gross and stupid and hilarious because I was so fat and faggy. I would have never said the faggy part and likely didn't come close to saying any of this to her.

> **But I did feel wrong. I felt like all I did was hide everything in my life.**

My dad didn't approve of or accept me. My mom barely did; she and her sisters mocked gays when they were together. I thought all I wanted was to be a TV star because that is what I knew best. If I were a TV star, then I would be somebody. All I had was TV shows growing up to make me feel better, so of course, I would aspire to be one. If I could get skinny, the gay would leave me somehow and I could be a sitcom dad. If I looked like a sexy straight guy, then I would be one.

I was lost in a cornfield, and my mind was like all the tangled leaves that crisscross like streamers when the wind blows. I tried to walk between the straight-as-an-arrow rows and follow the ranks of life in marching band formation. I had just signed up for the draft; it had started up again in 1983. It was a gloomy day when I felt like I signed myself over to someone else, which was a heightened version of how I felt for most of my 18 years.

All the rows in the farm fields were rows of the same everything, and all my soul wanted was a field of wildflowers and trees, but there are barely any places like that left in southern Minnesota. Cemeteries are the closest you get. Pretty places have no purpose, no point, and get plowed under to grow corn, soybeans, and oats to feed the cows and sell to "the man." When it blooms, alfalfa resembles a lavender field near Provence—I saw it in the *World Book* encyclopedia—but it soon fades and dries and gets baled into hay.

So, I continued to attempt to follow the rows of the cornfield, and the sharp blade-like leaves sliced at me, and the smut fungus, which is a nasty, nasty thing, got on my hands and spread everywhere. Bullies were hiding in the corn fields, and the fields go on forever in southern Minnesota. I couldn't find the end. That's what I thought and felt during my breakdown in the van, but I know there was no way I was that transparent to Mom. If only I would have tried. My mom and dad were smart cookies and compassionate souls down at their cores; they probably could have handled it and might have even been champs at accepting me. They might have been up for the challenge. Perhaps they just needed me to be the one to bring it up. Perhaps. But I was just too terrified.

# Chapter 5

## Leaving home

College sounded like being sent back to prison, but again, another necessary evil, as I had thought of my whole education up to this point. If I didn't head off to something, somewhere, what was I going to do? I could have stayed on the farm and become one of those bachelor farmers who was a hermit, but I had stars in my eyes, and thank God I did. Mankato State was only 45 minutes away, so I practically did plan to stay on the farm.

Then there was the whole problem of the dorm and the gang shower at college. Orientation was in June; I had signed up for the first possible session. "Look how different I'm going to be in college," I told myself. "I'm going to sign up first for everything and get along with everyone and get straight As and find a nice girlfriend."

The day came closer, and the images of meeting new people and sleeping in dorm rooms with strangers and showering naked with them haunted me. Mankato had big, high-rise dorms with 20 shower heads in a room; I learned this from a girl I knew who talked about her big girl roommate who set her alarm and got up in the middle of the night to shower alone. The group shower is such a brutal concept or is it our generalized American hatred of our bodies?

The orientation was the next week, and I hadn't lost a single pound from my unrealistic plan to starve myself into Parker Stevenson by the fall. If I could delay it a little, I could get serious and lose weight, so I called and moved it to July. But by then, I had gained 10 pounds. The scale arm swung free at 330 while clicking a little Morse code of "What now?"

I can't do this. I can't go to that big, bad Mankato State. All I could picture was people laughing and pointing at me. Horrible images of Carrie in the showers came to mind. Fat boy at the big university thrown out of the twentieth floor of the dorm was a horror movie in my head.

I could have walked in with an "I don't give a damn what you think of me" swagger. I could have just been happy with being the shy kid who lives in his own world and sits quietly by himself, which is who I am, but I had this damned need to fit in and prove to everyone I was more than what they thought. I needed to be someone folks took notice of and stared at in awe. My hunch is that this desperate need to scream "I'm good enough" was the sum total of years of feeling less than, mixed with wanting to feel okay just as I was.

This was at the core: I wanted to be myself and be okay doing so, which sure doesn't sound like too much to ask. When you are different in any way (fat and gay, for example), so much head and soul space is taken up with trying to fit in.

**Attempting to look and act like everyone else seems the surest way for insecure types to feel we're enough, and that we're good and worthy of love.**

And safe. The truth was, in rural parts in the 1980s (and still), you could get killed for being yourself, or at least get beat up pretty good. It's sad that so many gay farm kids run to the cities when in truth, their hearts are in the barn with the cows and the chickens, and their souls get jazzed at the sight of corn tasseling out and alfalfa fields blooming.

# A last-minute switch to a Christian college?

At the last minute, I went to the much smaller Bethany Lutheran College in Mankato, where ballroom dancing in the PE track was called social rhythms, and things seemed safer. The 340-pound gay boy who hated high school, but loved to dance, landed at a tiny college that was more like an evangelical high school and had a no-dancing policy. How did this happen? It was like I was trying to make peace with the high school horror in my head by doing it all over again and getting it right this time. The handbook stated that there were certain local establishments that students were not to frequent. The local X-rated bookstore, the only place to get gay nudie magazines, was one of them, not that I had the guts to go in and buy one.

At the end of move-in day, I stood in front of the cinder block cube of a dorm without one tree casting a shadow on it. It was like an oven baking 18-year-olds into who they would be. Most showed excitement, but I felt I was entering the fires of hell again. There stood the giant gay boy in a huge prison orange t-shirt and terrible jeans with a plastered-on smile. It was the first time Mom uttered, "I'll take a hug," and we did, and I could feel her sadness too, and a little shake in her body. Dad was quiet and hung his head. My sister probably knew best this was going to be bad and smiled tentatively.

The high noon sun cast my shadow on the pavement, and it stretched wide and long and made me even bigger than I was. The sun behind Mom, Dad, and Jodi cast their shadows on me. I didn't feel shadowed by them, though, just stitched together. We were more like four siblings than parents and kids, and they seemed sicker about all of this than I was.

# Driving under the influence of food

I fled the freshman orientation when they instructed us all to make a human chain by sitting on the knees of the person next to us. I grabbed the keys to my giant station wagon (a discard from Grandma's catering) and drove into the Mankato night, having a good old-fashioned nervous breakdown again, though it was probably more of a garden-variety panic attack.

> **The Hardee's had a new drive-thru window where I ordered a Big Deluxe combo with a giant envelope of French fries. I spoke anonymously through a speaker like it was a confession booth, and I barely had to look at anyone to pick-it up.**

I turned onto Madison Avenue, the main drag of Mankato, as I folded the bready, creamy, chewy gooeyness into my mouth. It was fast-food Valium.

Food was comfort, distraction, and it settled me down. The weight of the food added to the weight of me, settling my feet firmly on the ground, and I loved the ground. All I wanted was to be on the ground and in the ground and dig in it and plant things in it, but I had this thing that wanted more than that, and this landed me in places and situations that weren't really me.

Everywhere around me was food. There was McDonald's, but it was fancier than the Johnson family. Hardee's was small town. McDonald's was only in the big city. I did not speak the McDonald's language, but I pulled into the drive-thru, and I knew Filet-O-Fish from TV commercials and French fries are universal speak. As I pulled away, I tore open the paper, and it was hotter than food should be, but I went at it. I slipped further into a calm, dreamy state with the salt zapping me a little to keep me focused enough to drive, and the Dairy Queen was across the street in the parking lot of the mall.

The Madison East Mall was a happy place growing up. It was where I observed what was happening in the world. Yes, Mankato was the whole world to me. I bought pretty and flashy things there, like a hat with a blue unicorn horn. I stared at the glamorous mannequins in front of The Dahl House with the fake babbling brook I trailed my fingers through. I bought my Richard Simmons book at the BDalton and my K-Tel disco records at the Musicland.

I knew the Dairy Queen vanilla malt would coat my insides, soothe my anxiety, and take me elsewhere in my mind. I knew this from when I was six and the one avalanched all over and into me. My body wanted to puke it up as soon as I finished (it took less than a minute), but I forced it to stay down. I needed to feel it inside me.

I parked at an open end of the lot and laid across the enormous seat and on top of the nest of wrappers. What was I going to do? I fell asleep, or perhaps I passed out like I had just crawled the bars along Madison Avenue.

**I wasn't exactly a brave pioneer of my own life. I barely felt I had a right to the air I breathed. Everything terrified me, and I was so accustomed to doing whatever I needed to fit in.**

I thought to be a popular boy would be the best of everything; it would be the closest thing to a movie star I could get. It would make right all the stirrings inside me that I was wrong. Fit in somehow, Eric. That will make you feel better. Some men in my family would have hung themselves in the barn at this point, and I rather understood it.

I woke up in my car an hour later, and all I could think to do was drive up and down the steep hills of Mankato. Mankato is the San Francisco of southern Minnesota; the streets wind and rise and dive and turn, and I coasted down the hill to Lowertown and onto the highway. I drove into the great unknown, where maybe I could vanish, at least for a while, and end up in Miami to start an all-new life. But this was the 1980s, and I had no credit card. I doubt my new checking account and check blanks with kittens from Citizen's State Bank in Gaylord would get me very far. But Minneopa State Park was familiar and there it was. We camped there a lot over the years, and just a few weeks back when we toured the college.

I knew the bathrooms and the showers well, so I drove into the campground. It was late, at least 10 p.m., so I could have showered at the dorm, but I knew I would be alone at the campground. I had no towel, no shampoo, no bar of Irish Spring, but I had a couple of quarters. I parked where I wasn't supposed to, but it was late, and no rangers would be around. The back door went right into the shower, and it was dark and buggy, with mosquitoes going berserk in the muggy air that made it hard to breathe. Campground bathrooms always smell of creosote like on railroad ties.

The lights wouldn't turn on, but I knew my way. I dropped all my clothes on the floor and fingered my way around to drop two quarters into the slot like a gumball machine that got me a five-minute shower. They must have turned off the water heater because it felt like water from the garden hose. I shook under the cold, but it quieted everything racing around my head.

**This is what it had come to. Showering in the dark to hide everything I thought was wrong with me. But it numbed me, at least.**

I had no towel, so I dressed my wet body, got back in the wagon, and took off to return to horrible reality. Hardee's was open all night—so handy for types like me. I had a couple quarters left, enough for one of their enormous cones that get pooped out by a machine. I sucked on it like a baby on a bottle.

The campus was silent, and I crawled up the four flights of stairs and slipped into my tiny and bouncy dorm bed.

## A college degree in getting people to like me

Top-heavy was how I felt. I was the Bozo the clown punching bag that kids beat the crap out of. No one hit me anymore, but everything knocked me off my center. I felt like a twig in a creek floating fine and calm, and then the rapids would come, and I'd spin and bob up and down. If it got choppy, I'd go under.

"Hey, do you want to go to the mall?" someone would ask.

"Sure!" I'd say.

"Do you like to play foosball?"

"I do."

"Do you play Dungeons and Dragons?"

"Yeah." But that one I couldn't fake. I could never crack that secret society, and how the hell do all these guys know about this?

I had a fluid-like state of being that took me wherever the wind blew.

> **I did whatever I could to make others happy. That's how I'd get people to like me.**

This sounds so sad, but I was hopeful, and maybe that was the best thing for me to learn in my first year at college. I didn't need to be an outcast. I could make friends. I could be liked, and surprisingly, people did like me, at the risk of sounding like Sally Field's infamous Oscar award speech. I discovered, bit by bit, I didn't need to be a constant target. Out in the real world, people didn't behave like the pack of uglies at my high school. So, this is how people are supposed to act, I thought.

You might think that would stop the need to eat emotionally, but going for food was sewn into me. Oh, the silly notion I had that I would magically shrink because I was away from Mom's kitchen, and I would be too busy at night to eat. It was the opposite. I needed my anchor, my best friend, and my comforter more than ever.

> **I was the trust fund baby of food. It took care of me and kept me from growing up in many ways.**

The bank had called Mom about the many checks that came through with insufficient funds. She asked me about all the checks to restaurants: "You don't pay for everyone else when you go out to eat, do you?"

No, Mom, that was all me.

## Whose voice was in my head?

There were times I would hear a voice in my head say, "It'll make you feel better." Yes, I was experiencing the thing you see on movies of the week and Lifetime TV. I was hearing voices to eat. I was at a Christian college; perhaps it was evil spirits stirred up from the daily chapel services I went to solely to sit with my new pack of friends that was slowly forming.

I finally had some friends to eat with at lunch and supper, too. I could get as many seconds as I wanted at the cafeteria, and a couple of my new pals even got the giggles out of my second and third trips back to the food bar, where creamy, gooey concoctions shivered and wiggled in bowls. They were emotional aloe on my burns and salve on my constant invisible (and sometimes visible), nervous rash.

The voices weren't constant, or at least they were mostly muffled out during daylight hours, but in the evening, they began. I would break free from the crowd and drive to the Woolworth I knew so well from many trips to Mankato to shop for new school clothes and Christmas presents. The smell of new plastic all around and the bright fluorescent lights cast a fake but familiar otherworldliness to everything.

The bins of Brach candies seemed to glow radioactively. A quarter got me five, which would last long enough to try on the fake red Converse high tops or the grey plastic cowboy boots I coveted. Then in went five more, mostly the chocolate-covered cremes with pink and orange and lime green centers that were so sweet they hurt my teeth. They melted into a syrup and dripped down my throat like tequila shots; as soon as they reached my bloodstream, I was a goner.

**Brach candies were my gateway drug that sent me into the streets to hunt down my version of crack.**

I'd pick out a bag of Halloween candy and head to the car. No one thinks twice when you buy a bag of fun-sized Snickers in October. I cruised the main drag like the other kids did on Friday nights back in Arlington and got high with my bag of candy. I drove up and down and over to Mankato State and stared at the theater department building I almost went to. I'd end up down by the river, rather numb with relief. I'd return to the dorm to do whatever my new friends wanted. We'd order pizza or go to Walgreen's to get chips or head to Dairy Queen and I'd say yes, even though I was usually already loaded on sugar and French fries.

Maybe the voices in my head saved me. Years later, a shrink suggested that

55

all my eating in my teen years saved me from hanging myself in the barn, which ran in my family like diabetes.

## Hitting rock bottom in the mall

On the way home for the weekend, I'd often stop at the fancy downtown mall for a little day brightener. The JCPenney had big boy clothes, and Brett's Department Store had a killer clearance rack of XXXL shirts. I remember this particular trip so well. It was late fall tightening into winter, and the Benetton store set up in the center of the mall caught my attention. It was like an illuminated igloo in the middle of a dark woods, but I didn't dare go in. It was a store for other people, but I studied all the beautiful, thin, and smiling string beans on the posters in the window.

Someone was staring back at me. I knew him, but I didn't recognize him. I stared a bit more and then it hit me.

It was me.

I couldn't really see myself, though. I was a vampire in a mirror. I didn't seem to have a true reflection. I was huge. Incredibly huge. Winston Churchill huge.

I felt like a thing. A big pile of something on the side of the road.

> **I drove the hour home to the farm, where I ate like I'd never eaten before. I was a tornado picking up anything in my path and pulling it into my vortex.**

In went Mom's supper, something like Shake and Bake chicken (she liked the seasoning packet), and mashed potatoes, and buttery, salty corn. I cleaned up the pots and pans on the stove and picked through the garbage for discarded chicken skin. I inhaled Doritos and stale cookies shaped like windmills from the freezer and ice cream from the giant metal Schwan's tin. I stuffed in barely cooked bacon and mayo with a spoon and sugary peanut butter and tubes of Town House crackers covered with Blue Bonnet margarine.

Everyone was in bed by 10, and there I was, surrounded by walls of dusty, cigarette-grimy, and yes, beautiful and familiar knick-knacks in the living room. Our house looked like an antique store. I was back in my chair—a giant, brown, crushed-velvet marshmallow full of cracker crumbs smeared with years of jam, chocolate pudding, and Cool Whip. I sank into it, and it held me like no one ever had. No one hugged or brought their bodies close to one another in my family, but the giant chair did, and the food told me all was going to be okay.

**To eat and eat and eat keeps one in the moment. It's an odd mix of a mindful act while being completely detached from everything. It keeps you from dwelling on the past or fearing for the future.**

I kept making more and more peanut butter sandwiches and filling bowl after bowl of Mom's overnight fruit salad. I kept ripping open tubes of Pringles. I'd dredge the chips through a tub of sour cream and onion dip, and they distanced me from what was really bothering me. Like the Barefoot Contessa said on her cooking show: "You can be miserable before and after you eat a cookie, but never during."

I felt a weight of sadness around Mom and Dad, too. They seemed like turtles with sandbags or rocks piled on their shells. Could I be so arrogant to think that they were sad and a little off balance from my leaving? It seemed the happier and more at-home I got at school, the more sullen Mom and Dad got. I was finding my way a little, and then I came home and somehow felt guilty for being happy at college. Maybe it was mostly Dad, and Mom was a reflection of him. She couldn't feel any better than Dad did about anything, and that was our family in a nutshell. Dad was the high-water mark of the family. When someone is depressed, no one can have brighter emotions, at least not in the same room.

I ate until I could practically feel it pile up into my esophagus. Then the mindfulness ended, and regret and shame set in. To cope, denial tried to take over. Maybe things weren't as bad as I saw in the Benetton window? Perhaps I imagined the enormous someone.

Because the scale in our bathroom, that metal square the size of a box of Fanny Farmer candy, didn't go high enough any longer, I headed down to the barn in a walk of hope and denial to weigh myself on the feed scale that went up to 1,000 pounds. It was a giant, livestock version of the scale Mr. Klunder weighed us on in P.E., and I was as nervous as I always was during those humiliating moments that felt like a public stoning.

It was below zero, but I took off all my clothes and stepped lightly onto the platform, hoping I had imagined the refrigerator I saw in the window at the mall. Maybe the 10,000 calories I just inhaled were all in my imagination.

I slid the marker to the right until it balanced and though it was dark, a sliver of moonlight helped me see the number. It was an enormous number. I was 380 pounds.

I don't know if I was shaking because of the temperature or because of this number. I was alone in the middle of the night, in the middle of winter, in the middle of southern Minnesota, wrapped in the security blanket of fat I thought kept me safe. I did this to myself. I was responsible for it.

No one was going to save me this time, not that I thought anyone had ever tried.

# II

# Part Two

*How I lost the first 100 pounds*

# Chapter 6

## Self-esteem by association

I don't remember how the workouts began with JK, as I'll call him. He was my new Jock/ Homecoming King/Valedictorian friend, who I couldn't believe liked me. To walk side by side with him from the dorm to the weight room felt like my greatest success at the time. He was everything I dreamed of being. I mimicked him. He walked like men are supposed to walk, with a long stride, and his chest puffed up like an armor plate. His arms lifted slightly from his body to show off his biceps. A walk beside him across campus was the trophy I had always wanted. It was big man on campus second-hand smoke. I had a friend who was really something, and it made me feel that very adolescent word—popular. I was a movie star in my mind, if only a supporting player.

"I'm going to start you on chest presses. Work the big muscles first." I laid on my back with him above me, looking down at me with eyes the color of Aqua Fresh toothpaste. He knew this would be a tough one, and he lifted the weight onto my skinny yet fat arms. I wasn't scared. I knew he had me. I pulled up every bit of everything from inside me, and I pushed harder than I should have.

"Hey, you got this," he said, and he added weight, and I pushed hard again to try to impress. I didn't care about building muscle; I just loved being with him. Plus, I thought a muscled body already lived beneath my 380 pounds of fat—like marble waiting to be chipped off—which shows how disconnected I was from my body and how it worked.

He had me do sit-ups and it was like having Rock Hudson or Hugh Jackman hold my feet with their knees. How could I not imagine kissing him on each rise?

As if on a date, he took me to the soccer field down the street that was remote and deserted during the day. It was the kind of place kids sneak off to so they can make out and screw, but we ran odd little races.

"Go. Pour it on. Turn around. Stop," he'd yell at me. My side felt like when I suffered through the 600-yard walk/run in school for the Presidential Physical Fitness awards. Some kids gave it their all, but I just endured until the end, and the phantom knife stabbed me in the side, and the chest pain came like a heart attack.

Ten minutes into JK's weird exercises, I couldn't catch my breath, but I pushed through, sort of knowing this whole fitness thing wasn't going to stick. I was in my giant sweats Mom had sewed for me that looked like harem pants, and JK was in tight grey sweats, like a coach.

When I couldn't take it anymore, he put his arm around me. We were hip to hip. "Walk it off. Good job, buddy."

I worked out daily with the straight man I was secretly in love with. I was like a kid at Halloween in a ghost costume, with a white emotional sheet draped over me to hide everything inside I was afraid of, didn't like, and didn't want people to know. I cut holes out for my eyes to observe others and see how to act around them. It pains me now to think of it.

> **I thought a magic switch would flip when I got to a certain weight and a certain body.**

When I looked like all the guys in the shower, I would feel so sexy and like a real man that sex with a woman would suddenly be appealing. It would all come together and make sense. This was just one of many things I thought would magically happen when I got skinny.

*A peek into the future:* Many magical things did happen when I lost weight. So much in life got better and easier, but no, a person's core does not change;

it only reveals itself more, which is a magical thing in itself. More on this later.

## However twisted the motivation, it began the descent

I was back home for the summer after my first year of college. All was the same, but everything had changed. I was in love with a man, and I had to lose weight so he would think I was the greatest. It was only a slightly twisted take on why many of us try to lose weight—to look good to someone else.

> **I thought if I could make myself some variety of perfect, the result would be so damned appealing I would be a magnet; everyone would want to be around me, including him.**

He couldn't love me, but he could think I was the everything of all things in the world. Then all would be well. It was a twisted version of the rather sound psychological principle of transforming yourself into the thing you desire most.

But I was in a type of arrested development. This was 13-year-old thinking—to lose weight to win the boy—but at least my weight loss was in motion. The boulder had begun to roll. A little success breeds more success because of the confidence it builds, so whatever sets us in motion is worth it, I think, as long as we keep searching for deeper motives and try to uncover why we eat so much. Stay tuned for more on that.

Summer was in front of me, and this was it. This was the summer I was going to get skinny no matter what. To get skinny would be all I needed to figure out life.

I had experienced that when you lose some weight, you get the looks and the compliments and then the resulting good feelings. It was about 40 pounds lost throughout the spring. (At 18, and at my weight, that could practically happen in two weeks of not eating after supper.) When I felt shitty about myself, poof, I felt better from the kudos that came with weight loss. All the things I battled in my head and heart were silenced in that glorious moment of praise.

Kevin, who lived next door in the dorm, said, "Eric, you look so good, now keep going. You'd be the best-looking guy." This is what I heard: "You'd be the best-looking guy without all the ugly, bumpy fat on your legs and butt and the big belly that hangs like a fanny pack the size of a giant pillow."

Kevin was handsome and oh, the admiration and worship that good-looking people get. Life seems so much easier when you have that whole toolbox at your disposal, but it may have been a blessing that I was fat when I was young. With my yearning to be "someone" in the world, I might have been a real dick if I had looked like Nick Jonas. Also, being fat and ashamed of my body might have saved me from HIV that was running rampant in the gay community in the 80s. I had such a need to be loved, I would have let anybody do anything to me.

All I wanted was to get down to what I imagined was under all the fat, like I had seen on *The Phil Donahue Show.* It was an operation on a very overweight man, and they showed it all, which included big slices through what looked like many inches of the same fat that you rip off a chicken when you cut it up. The doctor had to stop in mid-slice and wipe off his knife like he was carving a beef roast. I watched the episode with Mom, and we were both mesmerized and horrified. Parts of it resembled the fat tail on the T-bone steaks I loved to eat the few times a year that Mom cooked them on the stovetop in a frying pan. I would eat any scraps of fat I could find. Dad and my sister didn't eat theirs, so I would turn invisible and go back to the pieces left on their plates and sometimes in the garbage.

**I imagined when I lost weight, the fat melted like a chunk of butter in a pan on the stove. I would grab and squeeze it and wonder what it was and why it didn't leave quicker and why I was the one to have to carry it.**

# Walk this way

"Holding Out for A Hero." "Girl's Just Want to Have Fun." "Let's Hear It for the Boy." These were part of my soundtrack for the summer at the farm.

I catered with my grandma many days, and I walked the gravel roads at night with a Walkman spinning cassette tapes I recorded off albums on my stereo. Duran Duran and the Go-Gos and Bananarama spun in my head. "Hungry Like the Wolf" filled my brain, along with the sweet, hot, grassy smell of a Minnesota summer.

I walked endlessly and faster and faster to the maniacally upbeat music. All the fantasy and glamour and bits of Hollywood and MTV videos twirled in my head. Madonna was in me. She was a hero to gay boys; we could tell she loved and accepted us. I imagined myself fit and glamorous and a little Bohemian, like she was in the early days, with scarves in her hair and little fishnet gloves and leggings, and what looked like sweatshirts tied around her waist. "Lucky Star" is an incredibly hopeful song. These nights were my first forays into shifting my thoughts to the positive. Again, stay tuned for more.

If it's possible to walk addictively, I did. I went amazingly fast, and then even faster, and I thought I could feel the little fat worms chewing and loosening my fat up as they moved around in my thighs and my butt. It's not a bad visualization, albeit a little gross.

Crickets chirped, and frogs croaked to the 1980s electronic hum. The pounding beat marched me forward quicker and quicker, and I would imagine the fat dripping off my thighs, and where it goes, I still wonder. Does it just evaporate, like bad thoughts? I would walk for hours, and then I'd slide off the headphones, the little foam cushions on my ears like Princess Leia's sidebuns. I would breathe in the pure air and let the bug sounds get into my head, and there were moments of real peace and happiness. I found hope and optimism out on the roads away from everyone back in the farmhouse I hid so much of myself from.

I walked the mile to the highway, then back, then a mile in the opposite direction, and then back. It was like the mile radius from the farm was the safe zone. Beyond was still a mean and scary place full of bullies.

**I loved many things about my life at the time, but overall, navigating the world was a walk on a high wire and caused me so much general anxiety that true joy and happiness and love were hard to find.**

When I walked on the roads at night, I seemed to chip away at this anxiety and somehow short-circuit the impulses that zipped and zapped me and caused me to lose my emotional balance. In this tiny, safe zone, I found walking to be magic.

A Nike poster back in the day read, "If there were more walkers, there would be fewer psychiatrists," or something like it.

**Walking is exercise and a therapy session at the same time. Something connects to a higher place when one walks. It's a direct line to help and a trusting dialogue with someone out there.**

My plea to those who are overweight is "Walk!" Start out tiny if you need to, like around the dining room table, but please begin. It has magical, life-changing properties, even when done very slowly. To this day, nothing helps me make sense of the world like walking. When I walk, I enter a different, higher head space where hope and possibility live. Good ideas appear. It truly is an alternate reality. It might be what we refer to as our higher self.

## Shiny objects to distract

Food was a constant and all-consuming presence in my life. Food was like having a puppy that never grows up. Anytime I wasn't actively eating, it showed up at my feet, begging to play. But there were times when I forgot about it, so I knew change was possible.

66

**Little golden moments occurred when I would get caught up in something, and food seemed to "get lost," as my mom always said to the barn cats who wanted to sit on her lap.**

Back in high school, I had written out a list of things to do instead of eating and hung it above my bed. It was advice from some teen health book I had picked up at BDalton. My sad list included awful chores, like building a fence for the sheep, shoveling out the barn, and cleaning my tornado of a closet. Who wants to do these things if they had the choice? This was my sad list of joyful distractions. I had actually compiled a list of things that made me want to eat.

But when I puttered around in the flower garden I planted that summer I pretty much forgot to eat. Gardening still magically kills my compulsion to seek out food. Walking endlessly to my mix tapes or biking the gravel roads with the dragonflies swarming around also did it. If I decorated my room, wrote endlessly in my journal, painted furniture in funky ways, or drew pictures of plants, eating didn't cross my mind. I lost track of time when I did all of these. Even a TV show or movie I was really into, like *That's Entertainment* on PBS, worked.

**To this day, I craft things to look forward to that will keep me occupied and away from my compulsive grazing. This is the secret to happiness to me: having something to look forward to.**

It works about 85% of the time and doesn't need to be anything huge. Heading to Target to find something cute and fun to hang above my washing machine will do it.

At the time (and sometimes still, to be honest), I had to wrestle myself into doing things I enjoyed, and why was this? I had an aversion to doing things that felt good. It was like I was punishing myself for being fat and gluttonous; I didn't think I deserved to do anything enjoyable. Anything fun had to be snuck in the side door. Enjoying things was foolish and indulgent, and that's how I thought of myself. Difficult and miserable activities proved I was somehow worthy.

> **I also had this subtle guilt feeling that to have fun was a family betrayal; how could I enjoy myself when Mom and Dad seemed to be suffering and unhappy in life?**

## Puke out those bad feelings

I had some very skinny eating days without trying too hard, and then sometimes I'd have to white knuckle my way through an evening. Only by way of sheer force and will I didn't eat. It was minute-by-minute sort of stuff. That's what it took to not eat and quite honestly, sometimes it still does.

To not eat was a fistfight and a wrestling match. It was a battle of something trying to work its way in or out. When I won the battle, the following day I would feel so light and empty and like a good boy. This motivated me.

But many nights, and always at night, I couldn't take it anymore. I'd throw a rock through the window of the imaginary wall I built around the kitchen. I'd crawl through and oh, the soothing comfort from potato salad and peanut butter sandwiches and so many Cool Whip containers of leftovers from Grandma's catering company. I would work my way through them and get doped up as I ate.

> **So much around me triggered angst and everything in me was hot to the touch. Food cooled it down.**

Then I discovered what to do. I could repent and fix the problem I had created. I knew how to exorcise the demons. Ice cream came up without even trying, so how hard could this be?

I would close the screen door silently behind me, find the tallest quack grass around the farm, and get rid of it. My mom and aunts gossiped about a woman in town who did it, so I basically got instruction sitting in on their coffee klatches. The first couple of finger pokes were like screwing with no lube as I shoved my dry, unwashed hand down my tight throat. I pushed and scraped, and a few gags happened. My whole body tightened and clenched to hold onto the food that had taken on a life of its own to me. I was rejecting a friend.

Forty or so shoves of three fingers down my throat, and up came the first eruption. It was like a saucepan of something coming to a boil and cooking over on the stove. Crackers, bread, cheese, potatoes, chicken bits, corn, and general fridge food soaked with milk and Diet Pepsi and coated in ice cream landed in a pile on the ground.

The first wave lubed my throat, so the second, third, and fourth exploded less violently. It was more like a gentle upside-down toilet flush.

**A lightness and feeling of euphoria followed. I had emptied my stomach, stripped myself of something dark and heavy, and redeemed myself. I had both created and solved a problem.**

Every time would be the last, I told myself, as I puked with fireflies all around me, their little butts lighting up bright Morse code messages that asked, "What the hell are you doing?"

Bulimia feels like you're living on another planet. It's an incredibly foreign concept to the body and the psyche. It's walking backward. It's sleeping during the day. It's amateur cannibalism, though you might make the case that anorexia is more cannibalistic while you eat away at your body via starvation. Bulimia is more like the game of Operation I played as a kid. I was operating on myself while I removed parts of my being I hated. When I binged and puked, I attempted to get the bad out. The bad feelings about myself, and the shame of being me, were puked out and flushed away.

If you're going to do it, there is a right way. It has a best-practice. Just bingeing and purging to get out the cake or box of Cheerios or tube of thin mints is not grounds for a good puke. It must be preceded by anxiousness over a life event, regret over past transgressions, or a bruise from someone's tirade. Then the feelings of relief make it worthwhile. It also makes the cold you'll get from your dirty finger touching the back of your throat—the spot where sickness is born—worth enduring for a week.

Once I did it in an ice cream pail on a rainy night and forgot it in the living room. Mom happened upon it and opened the cover and asked me about it.

I said I was sick and I guess I was.

## Back at school I got the love I was hoping for

At 19 and over 300 pounds, I could lose a pound a day and keep it off. Most days I walked at least an hour. I continually founds ways to distract myself from eating, and I constantly reminded myself how JK, my homecoming king crush, would hold me in awe when he saw the thinner me. I went back to college for my sophomore year at 290 or so. I hadn't binged and puked more than five times total over the summer, which in all honesty, was probably 10. Addicts minimize, but I did it only when I "messed up" and the food got the best of me, which was about once a week.

> **"Dang, look at you." I heard it a lot. All this praise lit a fire in me, like my pilot light ignited. Success breeds success—the saying holds true.**

When I went through the line in the lunchroom, I asked for only vegetables. "Oh, honey, you're not going to get fat off any of this food," said the head lunch lady who was the homecoming queen the year before. People tended to drop anchor at Bethany College.

There was a salad bar, and I would build a small haystack and mow through it like our goat, Winston, and then I'd get another and then another. It distracted me from the constant need to be liked and approved of by others. I munched and munched and was proud I only ate salads and vegetables in public. Mom made me homemade blue cheese dressing that I brought to the lunchroom; it helped my homesickness and made all the iceberg lettuce taste like something.

> **To this day, munching on mounds of salad is still in my weight loss toolbox. I understand why Elaine on *Seinfeld* was so in need of her "big salad."**

"Man, you look good." "Holy crap, you've lost weight." Every phrase was serotonin. I inflated with emotional helium and floated up and over the tiny campus of four cubes on a hillside in the city. I looked into the eyes of all the co-eds and I knew, or at least suspected, many would have nothing to do with me if they really knew me.

But for the moment, I was thinner and JK was my roommate. When I told people, I imagined they thought I was a big deal.

## Artificial sweeteners temporarily filled a hole deep inside

I begged my way into the title role in the play *Nicolas Nickleby*, which I was far too fat (and swishy) for. In the 1980s, you got cast as you looked. Nowadays, it seems more free-form.

I needed this part. It could be my ticket to Hollywood or Broadway or at least the Minneapolis theater scene. I saw every casting of any play I was in as a stamp of approval (or disapproval). If I got the part, I got what I needed to feel worth something. It would vaccinate me against feeling pointless in the world.

I told Sig Lee, the gentle, kind, and fatherly director, "I'll lose weight for it," and he looked at me with concern and love and said, "Do you think you could?" And then, like he caught himself: "But healthfully." So, yes, he thought I was too fat to play the Charles Dickens hero who carried Smike, his physically disabled sidekick, on his back like a knapsack. Sig smelled my desperation and gave it to me.

Sugar-free grape Kool-Aid was the answer. It became my Hydroxycut before there was such a thing. It gave me what I needed—a shock of sweetness to sugarcoat the world.

The sweetness was fun, friendly, familiar, and something to look forward to. The sugar stand-in filled the hole down inside and helped me love life a little more, or at least not hate it as much. This hole inside was very black. It filled my torso from the center of my chest to the top of my groin, where my belly had begun to drop from losing weight.

What was missing that formed this hole? What had been taken away?

**Perhaps there is a seed of self-love that we all get as a birthright, but mine never took hold and rotted, abscessed, and killed all the good feelings.**

To help this, I drank so much deep-purple Kool-Aid—uber sweet, cool, dark, and more like a plum taste. It tasted the way urinal cakes smell. It filled whatever was in me that screamed, "I'm lonely and scared and sad and lost."

Grape Kool-Aid turned my poop green, the color of baled hay, so I imagined it shifted the chemicals inside. Whatever is in Kool-Aid scoured fat off my body like a Brillo pad. (Of course, not really, but that's how it felt.) Rehearsals for a four-hour play took up a lot of eating time, as did the play itself on the two weekends it played, plus it was a lot of running and jumping. I was a very gay Victorian leading man.

Gallons of grape Kool-Aid and *Nicholas Nickleby* pushed me below 280 pounds. I got a roll of film back from the drugstore, and I looked taller than I was; it was like I had found a level of confidence and better posture from the survival of Bethany Lutheran College. It was a sort of two-year religious war. I knew a kid there who thought the Holocaust was a ruse. Many believed I was going to hell for being gay. I had made it through, and I was leaner. Perhaps holding so many secrets inside built some muscle. Anxiety is like doing constant sit-ups.

I had lost almost 100 pounds. Leaving Arlington seemed to pull the plug on the tub of my body, like I didn't need the parka I had layered on as protection from the Arlington bullies. Though I was eating less and moving more, I think about 75% of the weight loss happened simply from moving away. My psyche told my body it was okay to release the weight. The science of weight loss is clear, but sometimes I think extra weight is simply trying to tell us we need to make a change in life. When we figure out what that change is, the weight begins to leave.

Being 100 pounds lighter felt great, but I wanted to be thinner and then, finally, normal. It was all I wanted, but my addiction to food, my best friend, was still a block to getting there.

**I had lost nearly 100 extra pounds of security, but I still needed the 100 that wrapped me like a blanket.**

# Chapter 7

## I found my posse, but still felt like an outsider

I next landed way out west at the University of Minnesota at Morris, beginning with a summer stock theater gig. I hadn't planned it. I answered a call on a flyer, and then I was like Dorothy landing in Munchkinland after a two-year tornado at an evangelical college.

My schedule was a theater boot camp for 12 hours a day. If I wasn't in rehearsal, I built and painted sets, and made costumes, and hung lights. It always takes me a while to get to know people, so for supper every night, I walked alone the 15 minutes to the Dairy Queen for the new DQ sensation, the Blizzard. The Minnesota company named their new treat after the Northern winter phenomenon and it hit me like a snowstorm of sugar and dairy.

I walked back to the dorm as I scooped in my Hawaiian Blizzard with coconut, pineapple, banana, and whatever is in Dairy Queen ice cream. On many days it was the only thing I ate. I'm sure it wanted to fly out of my mouth like all ice cream did, but I held onto it. I needed it so badly. It numbed my nervousness via that big vein in the neck. It thickened my blood and settled me down. It made it easier to go back to rehearsal, where I expected the theater big wigs to yell at me about my puny voice and spastic body. Soon the other theater kids would discover I was a fraud, too, I feared.

But the craziest thing happened. I began to fit in. Spending all day in the theater around my fellow theater kids felt like when my truck settles into the right gear. Things began to shift into place.

When I went off to Bethany College, it was as if I had signed up for two more years of high school to try to make sense of those horrible years. It was an attempt to right the wrongs. I had tried to make a fit where there wasn't one.

This continued to be a pattern of mine for another decade or so. I continued to put myself in circumstances and with people that weren't me, as some sort of masochistic challenge. Also, I was so out of touch with who I really was, I didn't really know who the right people and places were for me. But my new theater crowd was like opening the door to a new part of myself.

**I was discovering life could be easier and I could be happier around the right people and in the right place.**

Mom, Dad, and sister, Jodi, came to see the plays and camped at the nearby Pomme de Terre park. "I just can't believe how much weight you've lost," my mom said with her cigarette between her two fingers. She surveyed me like she was a little suspicious of something. Several weeks of one meal a day, even if it was a Blizzard, and twelve hours of busy-ness, equaled at least twelve pounds lost, I would guess.

Dad was very quiet and tended to the fire. He never commented on my weight, like he didn't want to judge. It was like he understood. He knew the need for a bump in life and how important it was to have an escape and pressure valve you could open.

Coincidentally, I recall a camping trip five years earlier when my mom asked me what I would do when I needed to fit into a band uniform the coming year. She kept asking and pressing the issue, and it was Dad who saved the moment with, "Well, I bet you can slim down a little by that time." It was actual gentle encouragement, though I never slimmed down and had to squeeze into the biggest one they had. It fit the way doll clothes do on a cat in an Instagram photo.

Fall semester began and the new dorm cafeteria was a spread of food like Old Country Buffet. This place was not the prison food service of Bethany. It had a full salad bar the length of a school bus, with potato salad and chocolate

75

mousse, and an anonymous macaroni salad I loved that tasted like sugar and Miracle Whip. It had pizza and pasta and build-your-own sandwiches and the best of all, a soft-serve ice cream machine that was such a reliable companion. It was my therapist, confidante, and best friend at the new school.

> **Soft-serve ice cream was the kind of friend that I dreamed of but could never let my guard down enough to have. It was Laverne to my Shirley.**

I'd fill a bowl meant for soup, then scoop out at least a cup of peanut butter and swirl it in. I'd then top it off with a coating of sweet breakfast cereal like Sugar Pops or Golden Grahams. Then I was off to find my secret place upstairs in the food service building. The creamy, crunchy, salty, and sweet affair worked through the challenges of the day in this new, strange college.

> **Maybe I was meant to live the life of a hermit, I had thought. Everything hit me like a foul ball in the head, and any new experience smelled of doom and gloom.**

Goodness could be on the horizon, but not for me; I didn't quite qualify. Feeling good about life went to the first, second, and third place speech contestants, and though I was a finalist, I did not place. In the meantime, the ice cream concoction made me feel like a got a trophy for a little while.

I did have four or five new friends with whom I felt a warm BFF-ness. I had a few at Bethany, but I couldn't let the connection take root. I thought I had to keep my true self a secret for them to accept me, and I probably did. But I felt safe with these theater folks. They saw through me and seemed to know who I really was—and they still liked me. A couple were gay and helped me begin to say it out loud, at least to the people I knew would be okay with it. Coming out is most easily done in a pack. We're all best friends to this day.

**I felt strange and sort of ordinary at the same time and I needed to distract the rest of the world from seeing I wasn't all that special.**

"I wish I had a look," I told one of my friends.

"Oh, Rick, you do have a look." Rick was a nickname I picked up at Morris for a while. It felt good to step away from Eric for a bit.

"I do?" Like someone crowned me homecoming queen.

"Rick, you wore a pajama top for a shirt this week."

I curated a certain look and demeanor. If I was goofy enough and dressed oddly, people would say, "Oh, he's just a big, weird crazy guy." So, I acted the clown at the rodeo, a jolly Santa Claus who enjoyed all the fat. I tried to be big, merry, and silly, like I lived my life on a cotton candy island of fluff.

**No one could judge me too harshly for being fat if I appeared tickled to be so.**

## Thinner, but more exposed

As I began the winter of my junior year, I hovered just under 280 pounds. I had taken the little metal box of a scale from the farm, the one that maxed out at 280, and I hid it under my bed. I stepped on every morning after I peed.

I had moved out of the dorm and away from the food service buffet. I never ate breakfast, and I microwaved a tiny $1 vending machine hamburger in the student union for lunch. I spent the afternoon in the theater building doing homework, memorizing lines, and hanging out in the costume shop with my new friends. I'd usually take a nap at supper and then go to rehearsal. After, we'd all go for drinks and munch on endless cardboard bowls of free popcorn. I'd fall into bed, masturbate some stress away (I finally figured it out), drift asleep, and then start it all over again.

Of course, there were weekends at the farm when I jumped feet first into the kitchen and I'd eat like I was swimming in the food. I also had plenty of pig outs at school, as I still call them. There is no better way to say it. Pig out is a term I've embraced, along with fat.

I was in a very active play that winter, and along with a busy college theater life, my body melted through the bleak months that make Minnesota hard to live in. It happened despite eating my roommate's rice cakes and peanut butter like they were my own and free for the taking. Only at that age can weight slip off like it did.

One morning the dial of the scale, the little slot machine of my soul, spun to 265 and stopped. This was exciting, which is the sunny side of new and strange. The number felt like someone other than me.

265 is what I weighed in ninth grade. With at least six more inches on me, I looked pretty good when dressed, not that I thought it at the time. This is from photos I look at now. Below 280, I lost the look of someone who was overinflated. At 265 and six feet tall, I was a big, handsome-ish, Midwestern man. I looked like a Minnesota farmer, and you could do worse in life than land one of those.

> **Even though I had lost almost 120 pounds, I was still so damned uncomfortable in the world. Wasn't this all supposed to go away with the weight?**

The world was a suit that did not fit. It was the store-bought Halloween costume I got in fifth grade. After the summer of Mom's *Better Homes and Gardens* diet, I thought I could fit into one of the cool boxed get-ups with a cellophane top they sold at Woolworth. They were cheap little polyester jumpsuits and plastic masks with elastic strings, but it was my dream, maybe my biggest one at the time. I picked Grumpy, the dinosaur from *Land of the Lost*, but it was too small. I had to cut off the pants and wear it like a smock with the mask that hung cock-eyed and covered only a little of my chubby face.

# Are you there yet, God? It's me, the fat and insecure boy lost in the western Minnesota prairie.

Pretty much out of nowhere, my dad's heart exploded. He was gone at 49, and as you could imagine, it turned our family inside out.

I crawled back to college after the funeral, and I remember a night I walked the small city of Morris in the dark. Voices were screaming in my head that even leftover bags of funeral hotdish couldn't quiet. Walking was the only thing that somewhat shut them up. Eating just put a hand over their mouths for a bit.

Nothing seemed to matter anymore. I think it's harder to lose a parent you've had an incomplete or troubled relationship with; you not only have the black hole it leaves in your life, but you also dwell on all the "what ifs" and "if onlys" and "why nots" that swim around in your head. Then you entertain the biggest and most difficult question—did they want to leave me? Didn't they love me enough to want to try to stick around? My mom said something to this effect to me years later.

I was in a funk I couldn't imagine crawling out of, so I walked the empty winter streets. Winter was in full swing when the air is so cold it burns your nose, it snows all the time, and the snow cracks under your weight as you walk, which helps you feel like you're not alone. And now I lost a parent. My dad died, and again, I felt so different. No one who's 21 has a dad who dies.

Then, as if in a Hallmark Christmas movie, I looked down. There, written in the snowbank: "God loves you and so do I." I do not make this up. It was there.

> **I didn't know who God was, though. Whoever he was, I felt he abandoned me or more accurately, never showed up.**

I kept walking and I landed at the grocery store in town and bought my favorite pack of cheap, generic vanilla sandwich cookies. I went back to the old house I shared with two fellow theater majors, and dipped them one by one into water until the whole pack was gone, and the sugar eventually sent me into sleep. Nothing but eating seemed to have a point anymore.

I had brought back so many Ziploc bags of funeral hotdish that my mom had made, and then the church basement ladies burned when they reheated it. They had dumped it in the giant electric roasters too early and then blasted it on high too long. You just don't do that to Shirley Klucking Johnson's food; it was like ruining Julia Child's beef bourguignon the miraculous night she comes to dinner.

The hotdish was a paste of hamburger, stewed tomatoes, egg noodles, peas, corn, and carrots. The freezer at our theater house was packed with it, and all I wanted in life was to be soothed, to have something take away the sting of feeling like I was an alien from another planet.

**Because I was gay, I felt like a freak. Because I was fat, too, and now I had a dad who left me.**

Also, I was hell-bent on being an actor, as in a professional one after college, and sending the insecure into theater, especially when they don't have that full-on theater talent spark, is like sending kittens into a cage of lions. This had me on edge constantly.

But the hotdish. That felt like love and acceptance.

Food felt so natural. Eating was who I was. The taste and smell and feel of the food—that was me. It was what I knew best. It connected me to my body through my five senses, because I had no real sense of my body, except I hated it.

**Food made me feel a part of my body and the world. I felt okay when I ate.**

Eating to me was like how heroin addicts speak of their first hit and how it's what they'd searched for all their life. It makes them feel normal, I've heard said.

Normal to me was a plate heaped with funeral hotdish, then microwaved with half of a stick of butter on it, and then showered with salt. I'd sit in my bedroom, on the edge of the bed, and just be with it, not so much eating it as applying it to myself. It made me feel so good in the moment, like I stepped up on the stage, and the audience stood up and applauded my very being. Their smiling, cheering faces were exploding with joy. I was Bono. I was the pope. I was Barack Obama at the Democratic convention. I was adored and loved for every little part of my being.

I surrounded myself with food like many college kids do with empty liquor bottles stacked on a shelf like trophies. Eating was all I wanted to do.

## The Neiman Marcus cookie was my ecstasy pill

There's an urban legend involving the Neiman Marcus chocolate chip cookie. A woman supposedly ordered the recipe from the store for $2.50 but she missed the decimal and $250 showed up on her credit card. She made it her mission in life to give away the recipe to the world, and my mom wrote away for it after spotting a tiny ad in a local newspaper.

The Neiman Marcus cookie is divine. I think the secret is both chocolate chips and shaved chocolate, plus oatmeal and equal parts brown and white sugar.

I convinced the theater club to sell them at the winter musical during intermission. Several of us gathered one night and made 20 dozen or so that didn't sell that well, so the leftovers came back to our theater house for the cast party. Along with the cookies, the remains of the keg of beer sat for weeks in the unheated back porch, where it turned just a little sour, like a Red Wing crock of sauerkraut.

For weeks after, I partook in the very Minnesota act of sitting indoors but staring outside. I wedged myself into a lawn chair, one of the old timers with orange, green, and yellow webbing and a shiny aluminum frame. The whole thing was so light I don't know how it held me, and I had my rear so pushed into it that when I stood up, it came with.

I propped myself in front of the open door and stared at the backyard, and there is nothing sadder than a yard in Minnesota in March where the melting snow forms puddles with strange foam on top. The dead everything from the previous year unearths like skeletons, like a graveyard washed out. I drank cool, not cold, slightly sour beer that gave me the runs and ate cookies like potato chips.

> **The beer made me feel I was with Dad. With the cookies, I was with Mom. To eat naughty food and drink beer were family loyalties.**

It was a confusing family loyalty though. It was like my family wanted me to have some, but not too much, because then they looked at me with worry written all over their faces.

It struck me many years later that it wasn't that Dad or Mom wanted me to overeat and drink too much to the point that I was sad and full of regret. They just didn't want to be the only ones who relied on it to feel good in life. It was our family's way of being together.

> **This is what my body does when I eat goodies and drink alcohol: I finish the cookie or the glass of beer and something bubbles in my belly and rises up and screams, "More!"**

I become the baby bird in the nest opening my mouth wide when I hear momma or anyone approach. But then I feel like a big pile of shit after, like I did the dumbest, weakest thing in the world.

But still, I held out so much hope that this would all end and I would get skinny. At 265 and with a Bachelor's degree in Theater and English, I left Morris. I had found parts of myself through the help of fellow theater geeks in the middle of the farmland. I learned how to let down my guard around others. My heart softened, and I got in touch with my true self a bit more. This makes life better and more fun, but you also make yourself porous and more open to the outside world in the process. I had discovered how to be myself, but I did it in a safe environment. I soon learned that when you set out into the unknown again, it can feel like a constant emotional heartburn.

# Chapter 8

## A Master's degree in feeling crappy about myself

I found my way into a second-rate M.F.A. acting program not far from the farm and back in Mankato. Two weeks in all I could think was: Why do I have to feel so out of sorts and out of place and wrong wherever I go?

The first professor I met with one-on-one was an ex-ballet star from England. I sat in his office, and he looked me up and down, like I do with trees. I had the feeling I was going to get scolded.

"Look at yourself. How did this happen?"

What does someone say to that? So, I mumbled, "I know," and sat with my head down like I was in a confession booth. Lutherans don't have them, but we learn the concept at kitchen tables and teacher's offices.

"I mean, your sex life can't be very good." And at 22 in 1987, I thought I had to sit and take it. "No, not really," I said, ashamed and embarrassed by the very question.

He had been in the ballet, so he must have sensed the gay. I mean, this guy had been big in England. He has a Wikipedia page with "one of the top," "principal dancer," and "star" all over it.

"The typical American diet, this is what's going on here," he said. "Meat and potatoes, potatoes and meat."

He had no idea what he was dealing with. If I could have stuck to a typical diet of any kind, I would have been fine.

"You must have fresh fruits and vegetables. And you must do a complete personality inventory and strip your psyche down to the core." Or something like that. This was the gist of what he said, and with the last part, he might have been on to something. Actually, he was probably spot on, but I didn't trust him. I didn't trust any men, and certainly not straight men.

"What are you doing for dinner tonight?" he asked. This I wasn't expecting, and I stammered a little, and he mocked it good-naturedly. Maybe if I could have let Brit ballerina in, it would have helped me or at least made the next two years a little more bearable.

His dance classes were likely what kept me below 300 pounds because it was all a repeat of when I left the farm for college four years earlier. It was a food explosion. My every day and my eating were like someone lifted the cover off the blender and everything sprayed all over the kitchen.

My sad little Mankato apartment was a cube with four walls of fake wood grain paneling. The landlord gave me a can of light pink to brighten it up; it was the color of skin. One night I smeared a streak of it on the wall, stared at how blah it was, and then abandoned the project. What was the point of making the place nicer when I felt like hell? Instead, I got into my new Toyota Corolla and drove to the Hardee's two blocks away for a Big Deluxe combo.

I never had cash, so my checkbook register displayed endless checks to Hardee's for $3.25. Two checks a day on most days.

Every Friday night, I went home to the farm, and the first thing I did was get on the scale that I kept hidden under the couch in the living room. I ate like a wild animal all week which made me gain 15 pounds, but then my weight hovered around 280, and always, it shocked me. Brit's dance class, rehearsal for two plays, general grad school craziness, and being 22 kept my weight steady. Ironically, these were also the things that made me eat. Eating was all I could think to tame this crazy untethered feeling inside me. I searched for relief from the raging feelings of not feeling right where I had landed.

The farm was my retreat. I felt good around all my childhood things. I was peaceful and happy in the barn and with the old furniture and tools and vintage crap. I was at home around the weeds and trees. Oh, to get myself outside with that sweet, grassy smell that hits the back of your nose and dusts it like cocaine. It gives you that feel-good hit on your pleasure centers that I hear cocaine does. (Drugs never came up for me in life, and when all you want is food or booze to fill and quiet and calm, it feels so good to declare that which is not an addiction, though all it would likely take is one snort.) One weeknight, I drove home just to mow the lawn—I needed the hit of grass so much—even though I had a research paper due the next day and lines to memorize and an ancient play to read and the list went on and on.

**At the time, I thought I was just escaping the stress, but I think I was also running towards the things that I wanted more of in my life.**

Nature and the farm and cool, old vintage things with a history spoke to who I was deep down at the creamy center of my soul. But theater and grad school had planted themselves as "shoulds" in my life. They took up so much space there wasn't room for anything else.

Every Friday at three, I walked to the student union cafe across campus. In the spring, crabapple trees burst open in shades of pink; they were the Minnesota version of the cherry blossoms in Washington D.C. Petals snowed down on me during my magical little anticipation walk, like powdered sugar blew across my face, and I took in their scent. Friday afternoon was a time the campus got very quiet and nearly deserted, and I could relax a little.

At the cafe, I found leftover celebration cakes that were snow white with a thick frosting of powdered sugar and Crisco, and random swirls and lines piped in pink, yellow, and green. They were leftover bits of cakes from guest lecturer receptions, retirement parties, or student recitals. "Congrats" and "best wishes" and "we'll miss you" were hodge-podged all over the random fragments and wrapped in cellophane. They were 25 cents, 50 cents, maybe a dollar, and I could load up a tray with three or four; $2.25 and my life was sweeter and happier.

> **That's what sugar does—it makes life sweeter in the moment when you need it. After a while, you don't know how to make it sweeter on your own without the chemical help, so you go back for more and more.**

My friend, a fellow grad student, sold pencils and test forms to the Theater 101 class, and I would sneak into her coffee can of money and steal nickels, dimes, and quarters. I'd go to the vending machines in the cold stairwells of the theater building and load up on Grandma's cookies. They were incredibly soft and permanently moist from lard; when you left them on a paper napkin, a mottled circle of grease formed. They got me through long grad school days. I stole so many coins, and she needed to make it up from her own pocket. Once when she counted her money and ran terribly short, she said in frustration, "I bet it's Terry." He was a fellow fat master's student.

"Yeah, that seems like something he'd do," I replied.

> **I needed that cake and the cookies so much I stole to get them. Nothing seemed sweet or lovely or divine at the time. Nothing even felt just plain old good or even fine.**

## Aspartame to the rescue

I asked myself in a rather clear moment, what if I could just not eat after rehearsal? But I needed a hit after a night in the theater, which always felt like I was on trial. Most nights when I got home, I'd sit down with a loaf of cheap wheat bread, which is just brown, white bread, and a tub of peanut butter. I'd feed on endless peanut butter sandwiches, one after another, like a deck of cards I played solitaire with. But what if I could find something that gave me the release and the hit of sweetness but without the 2,000 calories I would inhale?

How about the sweetened, powdered, lemony Lipton iced tea Mom always had in her cupboard? The idea landed on me like a mosquito. Wow, that stuff was sweet, especially if you didn't add as much water as the label said. I tried it and magic happened—I had a happy little sugar dance on my tongue. I would come home and pull out my jar of magic powder and it gave about 75% of the feel-good hit of a cookie. It gave me a similar lift and also, felt like a friend was with me, helping me, and talking me through the challenges of the day. The friend part was and is a large part of my emotional eating.

**Food is a companion. It's a buddy when I'm stressed or guilty or all-around nervous. Having it with me and inside me makes me feel better and less alone.**

Surprisingly, low or no-calorie food seems to work pretty much the same as sugar and carbohydrates in giving me an emotional lift. I am lucky in this way.

I'd crack the tea jar open and peel back the vacuum-sealed foiled paper that released a little fairy dust cloud of the powder. The smell hit me as it rose to my nose, prompting a sneeze. The chemical, lemon, and acid smell burned; it was a whiff of something that scours things clean. It helped with my feelings that always felt like low-grade flu.

The tea gave me a little lift without the regret, and when I drank a lot, which I always did, it caused a monsoon of diarrhea that felt like a purge of my bad feelings. I felt like I had found my magic powder. A slow drip of sweet tea at the end of stressful days seemed to give me what I needed most or at least kept my mouth busy.

This was hardly a health best-practice, but it was one small thing I did to steer me away from going to food. It was a fair trade at the time. No, the tea wasn't great for me, but it was way better than a loaf of peanut butter sandwiches or two Hardee's Big Deluxes at midnight. It was a small step forward.

> **To this day, making just one change and then focusing on that one thing, has been the biggest part of my losing weight.**

A recent example is giving up the whipped cream cheese that somehow had become a staple in our fridge; a few random scoops in a day brings a couple hundred extra calories.

One small (or not-so-small) thing done by itself works for me. Full-blown makeovers have always been too much of a tsunami.


## What other fat people showed me

There was another big guy in the theater department. He was a mountain of a man—at least 400 pounds—and I got all the roles he wanted. He was good, but he was too big. I was functioning big. He threatened and disgusted me because I saw myself in him; fat people are sometimes the least empathetic of other fat people. We humans are least tolerant of the things we refuse to see in ourselves or the things we do see, but hate. At times, I was sympathetic of him because I knew what he was going through. He was bigger than I was at my heaviest.

He once walked in on a guy making fun of him, and I witnessed his inner workings. He cornered him against the dressing room wall. "You like making fun of me, huh? Do you?" He screamed and barked like an abusive husband about to punch his wife in a movie. "You fucking got something to say to me?" His face puffed up and turned red and wet; it looked like how I remember pitchers of cherry Kool-Aid to look in the summer as a kid. "You don't fucking make fucking fun of me you fucking little piece of fucking shit."

The dressing room turned silent, and the kid shrank and turned into a four-year-old. "I'm sorry, I'm sorry, "I'm sorry." Big guy is now dead, and the other guy is a big-time actor who was on the West End in London.

I understand big theater guy. When you grow up fat, you are very aware of your body. People are always referring to it, and eventually, you explode.

Some of the phrases I heard as a kid: "Boy, he's a little porkchop." "You like to eat, don't you?" "Oh, look at the little football player." The last one I really hated. It's why I don't like sports to this day.

You become very aware of your body. Soon you are overly aware.

> **You grow to think the body is everything and your brain and heart and soul don't have any say or power or voice. You think that all you are is your body, and you made it, and you fricking messed it up.**

I made my body, and I was ashamed of it. I felt all alone. No one was there to help or take care of me. Prayer was pointless, and hope got dashed the next day in PE or acting class. Walking down the street and hearing the random "Fatso" or "Fag" or "Whoa, there's a big one," continuously chipped away at me.

I was in adulthood and not tapped into anything beyond my five senses. I was (and still can be) so focused on my body, and I think that's why I couldn't connect to any sort of spiritual presence. God was just a concept to me. I had no way to tune into my inner compass. It was all about the body. The giant, fat sack I sat in.

## A little mental reprogramming

A tall, slim character actor from Minneapolis who slept with women, but I could tell was gay, was my best friend. We played the Laurel and Hardy-like characters in *Guys and Dolls*. During my final months of grad school, we were roomies in a third-floor apartment in a building that looked like the White House and always smelled of dirty diapers and frying hamburgers. He was such a good friend, and he could tell I wanted to lose weight so much.

"I have to love myself, you know? Love my body," I said to him. It was something I read in a magazine article. I impulsively grabbed all the women's magazines with "top ten tips to lose weight" and "change your life" on their covers.

"Well, isn't that more of a process?" he suggested. It was honest, compassionate, and pretty spot on, but he was tall and thin. Did he really understand the whole emotional eating thing? He introduced me to Rondos, the little ice cream bon bons. We laid in our beds at night and worked our way through a carton. I knew I couldn't do this and lose weight, though I did have a denial about eating little treats. I thought that if I wasn't stuffed, then no harm was done. "Maybe you could have two?" he suggested, not knowing what he was dealing with.

At BDalton bookstore, I happened upon a rack of subliminal programming tapes. Quit smoking. Stop biting your nails. Eliminate procrastination. Then a fanfare and a spotlight shone on one—Lose Weight. $10. Money-back guarantee. All I had to do was listen for 30 minutes as I fell sleep. What a find, I thought. This was going to shift my fat cells, clean out my nasty, trashy brain, unclog my blocked being, and finally, once and for all, make me right.

Terrible dreams began, but the first wasn't too frightening. It was a dream but very, very clear; it was like a hallucination in that twilight time when you are about to fall asleep. I was crawling out our bedroom window with a huge white lumpy butt in baggy white Fruit of the Looms. It was more comedic than scary.

The one that shook me was a hazy vision of cruising along a highway. I wasn't in a car, but like a hawk soaring along, and I came upon myself in the middle of the road. I had a bloated, bleached, whale of a body, as if washed up after bobbing in the water for weeks, with a deep red gash across my belly. I woke like I had witnessed a murder.

I returned the tape and exchanged it for a cassette of the greatest hits of Bananarama, and the pop rock beat got me walking again, like I had done in summers past. Soon I was going very, very fast without even trying and I entered an altered state, like the weight loss tape, but lighter. I spent an hour, or sometimes two, at this higher altitude every day. It was a mental reprogram to "I'm On Fire," "Forever Young," and "Robert DeNiro's Waiting," and it felt like it knocked some bad stuff loose inside.

When I was walking for a long time to that groovy beat, I just didn't give a damn what anyone thought about me, and I would whisper a gentle dash of fuck you to all the voices in my head.

> **The fast walking to happy music cleared my head and nudged me to a higher, lighter state that seemed to stick with me until my next walk.**

I got so clear I felt good about myself, at least for a chunk of time. I even cared less about the random shitheads out there. Walking to Bananarama seemed to have magical powers.

I weighed myself daily, and in two weeks I had lost ten pounds. This brought me back to a solid 280, after playing an endless game of catch with 20 pounds during grad school. I had lost 100 pounds and had kept it off. The first 100 was the easiest, though. The second hundred stuck to the ribs, but I still held out hope.

I had a feeling, which might have been just really ardent hoping, that my next chapter would bring a big change. When all you've known is college life and living with your parents, setting out into the real world is like jumping into a Minnesota lake in December. It's a shock to the system but it does kickstart change. Nothing would feel the same again.

# III

# Part Three

*The second 100 pounds lost*

# Chapter 9

## The move to the Twin Cities

Mary Tyler Moore is the reason so many Minnesota farm kids land in the Twin Cities. I've heard others say it.

She was so thin, pretty, plucky, and had great clothes and a bright, happy everything about her. Plus, her cool old Victorian apartment near the Minneapolis lakes, with a great and artsy Bohemian best friend upstairs, was a dream. I wanted her spunk, cuteness, wit, and a job where everyone adored me and were, most likely, secretly in love with me.

After I moved to the city, I tried to be a version of her. I searched for waiter jobs as I touted my catering experience with Grandma, but the faces of the managers dropped when I walked in. Their smiles wilted when they saw the 280-pounder in women's clothes. (I hope it passed as men's, it just fit me better). I tried to be plucky, like Mary, as I spouted an over-animated "I love people, especially kids." I bet they saw through my act and could tell both were big fat lies. More likely, they didn't want a big, fat fairy around the place. It was the 90s. The thing was, I didn't even want to be a waiter, but it seemed like the thing to do if I was going to try to be an actor. To be a waiter and a wannabe actor was a common pairing I saw on TV.

I don't think I wanted to move to Minneapolis either, but Mary Tyler Moore made me do it. Also, I wanted to be a theater star, or even better, in a TV commercial. Then everyone in my high school would think I was a big deal, not the joke of a sissy, fat boy that I was branded. "Look at me, I'm something.

Finally, I am somebody."

> **Way back in grade school, I remember I needed the world to validate me. I needed to get my sense of worth from something or someone else, and the scrambling to do so kept me on emotionally shaky ground.**

Maybe I was born with a deficit of it. I was a little boy who hung in the shadows and seemed always to be afraid to jump in the pool, play with the blocks, and do the art project the way I wanted to. Many of my drawings as a little kid were started but never finished, and all were single, solitary figures. A tree in the distance. A kitten by himself. A small circle in the middle of a blank page.

> **It was as if the world wasn't a fit for me, like I entered through Mom's birth canal into the wrong delivery room, and on the wrong planet. Nothing was right. Everything was off.**

The light was harsh; I hated sunshine up until I was in fifth grade. The ground was broken glass. The air burned. I clung to the edge of the woods, figuratively and literally, and that got so lonely I tried every way I could imagine to be a part of things and fit in. How could I adjust myself and be a part of this world that seemed so off?

At least I forged ahead in my life and didn't crawl in a hole at the farm and eat and eat. As uncomfortable as I was in the big city, I was hopeful things would eventually shake themselves out. I really did have an optimistic nerve running through my body. It was a sciatica on the sunny side of the street with general hope for the future, and where the hell did that come from? Mom had it. She really did. You can't upholster couches without some vision of the future.

# Until I figured it out, I had Oprah, ice cream, big muffins and sugary margaritas

I fell in love with Oprah at the time. This was the Oprah who was big, like she was in *The Color Purple*. This was the Oprah the world and I fell in love with.

**Fat people trust other fat people.**

She was a mix of a mom, a good friend, and a therapist who showed up every weekday for an hour after work or school. We felt like our problems were also her problems, and she talked us through them. Plus, she came to visit at the perfect time in Minneapolis. 4 p.m. is the witching hour when we need to transition from work to play. It's the time of day that birthed happy hour.

I would usually walk the nearby cemetery after whatever temp job I had and before her show. It felt safe as I looped in circle after circle over a single square mile, much like I walked the gravel roads near the farm. No one bothers you in a cemetery. I was alone with my thoughts, and the hundreds of other lost souls joined me in my sadness, but they did not judge or comment. They simply walked along with me.

Walgreen's drugstore was halfway between the cemetery and my apartment. Not every day, but at least once a week, I tucked $2 in my shoe. I told myself every time would be the last. I knew it wouldn't be, but I hoped.

Walgreen's had the classic drugstore smell—a mix of aspirin and Windsong perfume. This Walgreen's played the current Top 40 and many times, more than averages allowed, Wilson Phillips sang to me: "I know there's pain. Why do you lock yourself up in these chains?" In the back, past the row of greeting cards and near the counter where you dropped off your film to be developed, was a row of freezers.

The vanilla cubes were the best because they came back up nice and clean. I made sure I was back for Oprah at 4, and then I would microwave the cube for 10 seconds. I'd drop it into a very large mixing bowl and start to swirl it around and around. I've heard meth addicts like the swirl of smoke in the glass bulb of the pipe as it gets their adrenaline rising; mine did when I saw the ice cream get soft and creamy. So much calm and soothing sweetness and comfort was about to be felt as I sat down on my sad little couch with a blanket tossed over it to be with Oprah. It might have been the familiar ritual of it as much as the ice cream.

The 5 o'clock, channel four news in Minneapolis has the same opening theme song now as it did in the 90s. When I hear it, I think of the geyser of foam and stomach acid flying out of my mouth and back into the bowl. When I ate a bowl of ice cream, it soothed my insides, and then it all came up, and I didn't need to suffer the calories. Everything felt like it was going to be okay. It was the answer to all my problems. Like other forms of self-harm, cutting for example, puking releases a chemical feel-good something inside.

To eat and eat and eat was my only way to feel safe because to me, the world was not a safe place. Minneapolis felt unsafe on a mammoth scale.

**To go to food was the only way I knew to handle fears and insecurities, and I had been doing it since I was six.**

Now I was out in the world trying to make my way, and I was doing it like a six-year-old boy.

\* \* \*

I read a story of poor Judy Garland and her intense addiction to pills. Someone had once dropped one of their prescriptions on the floor in front of her, and she immediately dropped to her knees to get it. It was like that game where someone lays down a card, and everyone slaps their hands down on it. That was me with free food in the lunchroom, perfectly fine food tossed in the trash, free samples at the grocery store, and pretty much any food in general.

My heart lights up like ET the Extra-Terrestrial when I see it. It's chemical. It's an addiction at its strongest and most unyielding.

> **Food addiction lives in my body like a magnet. Sugar is the strongest pull. Alcohol has a pull, too, which is mostly sugar and has the same calories per gram as fat, but alcohol doesn't fill the hole deep inside like food. It only numbs it for a bit.**

Every time I stopped at Cub Foods, which was pretty much daily, I would get one of their glorious muffins. I called them a treat, but they were little buffers against the world. My favorite was the orange blossom that tasted like it was baked full of Kool-Aid. The morning glory muffin presented itself as healthy—it was full of raisins and visible carrot shards—but when you set it on a napkin, it left a circle of grease. The glorious lemon poppyseed muffin was so sweet and lemony strong it tasted like it was sprayed with Pledge furniture polish. These muffins were my joy, my sex, and my best friends. They were like a pet dog waiting at the door when you get home to lick your face and love you. Each was probably nearly 1,000 calories so they were also a tight plug in the drain of my losing weight.

Once the checkout asked, "Do you have the munchies? Are you depressed?" Then she added, "I like your coat."

Two of my old college friends made these margaritas that were tequila, triple sec, and Rose's lime juice and were so sweet and limey and boozy. I looked forward to them as much as I did seeing my friends. They were like drinking sugar cookies, and very soon, like in three minutes, a warmth started to take over my body, like an electric blanket wrapped around me, and someone was on the control and slowly bumped it up. The warmer I got, the more I settled into my chair, and three-quarters of the way into the drink, I started to think, I am okay. I can do anything. I would imagine myself as I entered the stage in a packed theater in something dramatic like a Greek tragedy. I played the woman who killed her children to get back at her philandering husband with drama at the level of Faye Dunaway as Joan Crawford in *Mommie Dearest*. Sugar laced with booze gave me this fantasy confidence in my head.

Four margaritas went down easily; 280 pounds of flesh can soak up a lot of tequila. I'm sure I smelled like the carpet in a VFW as they processed out of my body, and I sat with the regret as the good feelings wore off, and I thought about the thousands of calories I had consumed as quickly as drinking a glass of water.

> **They tell us that sugar is more addictive than cocaine. The dopamine it releases is an enormous upper.**

It's pretty simple science. Eating carbohydrates boosts the brain chemical serotonin, which prompts us to relax and feel happy about life for the moment at hand. The few minutes during the piece of pie, and the fleeting 15 or so before the wave of regret washes over, are glorious.

I had come to believe that our happiness circuits get fried by years of overeating. The body's own ways of making the world bearable or bright just aren't there anymore; it's like the fuses get blown. But I have to believe we only trip the circuit on our body's ability to produce feel-good hormones. We can get it back. Without this, change seems hopeless.

## Stuck in the temp job of life

I feared that if I got skinny, I would lose everything that I built my actor persona on. My fatness was 85% of the characters I played. My size and my weight did so much of the work for me, and as much as theater made me uncomfortable, it was my every wish.

Everything in my life felt like one big temp job. I couldn't make a living from the theater because, honestly, I didn't really have "the goods" to do it, so I needed to find jobs to support myself between my few paid acting gigs. I couldn't get a "real" job because I might need to audition at a moment's notice. I could also potentially get a tour or a summer stock gig out of town for a spell (which I did) or something that rehearses during the day. This left me taking jobs that were awful and boring. Everything in my life seemed temporary and built on sand.

This was also the way I felt about my body. My embarrassing body and silly self were only temporary. "Don't look too closely or take me too seriously because what you see will all change," I told others, in my head.

> I hated how I looked and honestly, was lukewarm about who I was, but I had no idea how I was going to change because that meant losing my food crutch.

I would have had such a different life if I hadn't always wanted to be something or someone else. Or maybe my path wouldn't have been all that different, but it would have felt so different.

> The most harmful part of being overweight might be the lack of self-love and acceptance. Are there some fat people who have it? I mean, really and truly? I hope so, but I never did. All I wanted was to be something different; then I could love and accept myself.

I was in a constant state of this is not really me who you see. I'll just be silly and goofy, like the big happy fat guy, and then you'll at least be nice to me. But don't think for one second that this is the real Eric. Stay tuned for the real me to emerge, and until then, don't hurt me.

I also feared that if I relaxed into myself and declared I was okay as-is, I'd just eat and eat and eat. Striving to be something and someone else is no way to live, but it may have at least kept me from gaining back the 100 pounds I had lost. I was thinner, but stranded between who I was and who I wanted to be.

So, is it possible for a very fat guy to have a full and happy life? I mean really and truly? Can he have self-esteem, self-worth, self-confidence, and all those terms in the books on the top shelf I seemed to be too fat to reach? Self-actualized sticks in my head from Psych 101. As I understand it, it's someone whose basic needs are all met (including psychological needs), and they are rockin' everything they want to in life. Can you be 280 pounds and also be self-actualized?

**Isn't morbid obesity a big red flag that something's off inside?**

I so understand how people can't seem to rise above certain situations in life, like obesity, dead-end jobs, and bad relationships. I had felt stuck in the mud of excess weight for decades. Many years at 280 pounds left me feeling like this was it; 280 was my life sentence. Even though I had lost 100 pounds, it seemed like my lot in life.

**Here was the quandary: I thought if I could lose 100 more pounds, then I would have the confidence and the wherewithal to do anything I wanted. But I needed that elusive confidence to help with my emotional eating.**

Did everyone who was fat think as much as I did about what it would be like to be thin? Did it consume their thinking as much as it did mine? Then the big question: if it was all I thought about—which it was—why did I not do something about it? Why didn't I dig in and grab on and make it my everything, all-consuming purpose? Why not craft a diet and a workout plan, and then forge ahead without one thing getting in my way? Bottom line, I needed the release of the emotional eating too much.

## Voices in my head

I had voices in my head, and I still do. Mine don't yell at me to jerk the steering wheel left into oncoming traffic or to jump off the top story of a parking ramp; they're more like a pack of little kids needling me. They're a third-grade class in my head questioning, "Why did you do that?" They tell me, "You can't have that," and they ask me, "Why did you say that?" They need constant attention. Food, and also alcohol, quiet the kids because I think I need to give them all the attention they beg for.

I needed my soft, squishy suit of armor I thought protected me from the voices. I imagined it deflected bullets and bounced them away, like pitching baseballs at the trampoline-type device in the Sears catalog that you could throw a ball at, and it came back to you. When I was 10, I thought if I got one of these, I could learn to like baseball and then somehow be accepted.

But the joke was on me. The extra pounds that clung to my frame were more like a mattress, and when I got a hit, it went thud. It stuck and sunk in and got infected, sending a toxin through my body. This might have happened if I was 165 pounds. That's how I process the world.

> **I take every word or action as a bullet and a personal attack. It makes me feel like a constant outsider and it makes me want to eat.**

But when I imagine a life that would ensure me not getting looked at, pointed at, made fun of, and cast out, it seems so damned boring and beige I can't imagine it. It's khaki golf pants with a royal blue polo shirt eating at Applebee's. It's an office job in a tall building pushing paper with a bland happy hour after, then going home to watch boring TV, and mowing the lawn on the weekend, and snoozing through church on Sunday. Imagining that kind of life made me realize I didn't want to fit in.

> **All I wanted was to be myself and to feel comfortable and safe doing so.**

I wanted to be left alone to be myself. And I wanted a break from all the fat; the big belly, thighs, and boobs simply wear on you after a while.

## Food distracts from the boredom of a dull job

My temp job at the cellular phone company had become permanent, and soon there were bonuses and Circle of Excellence trips to Florida and the golden handcuffs, which for me, didn't take much. A job with health benefits and paid sick time made me feel like a Rockefeller.

My food work days were rote. I warmed a cinnamon raisin bagel in the microwave and added enough Nutra Sweet and powdered cream to coffee to make what was basically a hot malted. I never planned lunch. Corporate America throws away so much food I could always scrape together something to get through the afternoon. There always seemed to be a leftover aluminum sheet pan of fried rice sitting in the lunchroom.

And how could I ignore a random box of doughnuts? They were always popping up, left over from meetings, and this one was abandoned and perched on the top of the garbage. To me, it was like throwing a bag of kittens into a river.

> **I envied the people whose adrenaline didn't rise when they spotted orphaned sweets.**

Video cameras weren't everywhere like now (I hope), and I couldn't let what I saw as a box of friends be tossed away. I pulled it out of the trash can, and it so easily slipped into my file drawer behind the hanging folders. I snacked on the doughnuts through the endless afternoon, like popcorn at a movie. It killed the corporate job numbness and filled the emptiness of eight hours of faxing and photocopying and getting sales reps to fill out paperwork completely. The doughnuts distracted me from how bored I was with what I did all day. They added sparkle until the self-disgust, loathing, and regret kicked in, which also occupied my mind.

## Puking my guts out: the end of bulimia

A couple times a month, I'd still stop at the grocery store on the way home from a bad day. A quart of ice cream and a pack of vanilla sandwich cookies and you can guess the rest. It was a half-hour of hysteria when I'd melt the ice cream a little in the microwave, and the smooth sweetness was so soothing and also, fun. It wrote a poem in my insides that all would work itself out. It took away the sting and the burn I felt from people and shook me out of my boredom from the day. It cooled the burns from the emotional cigarettes put out on my skin.

I'd dunk all the little sandwich cookies in water so they'd get soft, and eating them felt like someone rubbing the top of my hand to quiet me down. They stopped the mania that bopped around inside me like a pinball.

> **Eating disorders such as overeating and bulimia work so well in the moment. They feel so dang good and take your mind off your troubles so completely for that little while.**

The food is yummy, and the temporary relief so sure, how can you not get hooked?

Now that I had insurance, I went to the dentist; it was the first trip in many years. In my dazed gas and Novocain haze, I heard him say to his assistant, "I wasn't expecting that." They had to replace several of my fillings and give me a bunch of new ones. All the acid ice cream and cookie puke had eaten away at my teeth. "Do you drink a lot of Coke?" he asked.

"Guilty," I said, all goofy and fake sheepish.

When I puked, I felt about half a notch above someone who kicks dogs. In addition to your teeth going to hell, your stomach seems to forget how to process food, so you bloat for a week after and have a constant raw, sore throat. Your face and ears and nose throb, and it feels like your esophagus is trying to crawl out of you.

And it's just so plain disgusting, especially when I would get it all over me. I would vomit into the kitchen sink and then scoop it into a pail to haul up to the bathroom and dump into the toilet and the toilet would clog and I would spend an hour flushing and plunging to get it to disappear, though the smell lingers for another hour.

Nothing else I've ever done to myself caused more shame. I did it on and off for about ten years. I don't know how anyone does it any longer than that, and with my obsessiveness over things, there isn't much I can say that about.

It's been one of the greatest gifts in my life that it sort of just went away. And it really did just go away on its own or at the hand of angels or a plain, old-fashioned miracle. All I can say is thank you, thank you, thank you. I know of two older women who did it until they died.

I did get a slap in the face from up above that scared the hell out of me. It may have been one of my guardian angels pulling the need to binge and purge out of my body. I was out walking one evening, and like a lightning strike, a phantom sword impaled me from my groin up into my stomach, through my chest, and into my throat, *Game of Thrones* style. Yes, that sort of thing gets your attention. I remember the feeling 25-plus years later. It's one of the top three pains I've ever had.

God's not tapping on your shoulder or whispering in your ear at that point. He's grabbing you by the balls and yelling like a high school football coach, "Get it together."

# Chapter 10

## Shifting to a more positive point of view

Out of nowhere, a friend from grad school gave me a book—*Creative Visualization* by Shakti Gawain. Three pages in, I felt something shift, like the soft click into place when a puzzle piece finds its spot. Something grabbed my inner steering wheel and cranked it to the right. I turned a corner onto a nicer street where flowers grow everywhere, lawns are greener, and someone painted all the houses bright colors. It seemed to say, here's another way to look at things. It shifted something inside in an alarming, but good way.

> **I've experienced it many times in life when things sort of land like magic. The secret is to keep your eyes and ears open and not quickly dismiss them, because they can seem random and irrelevant.**

One chapter into *Creative Visualization*, and it dawned on me—good things could happen, too. It got me to think that I had a hand in how my life went and maybe most importantly, how each day could go. The upside of being highly impressionable by the negative in the world is you can also go to a positive place pretty quickly when prodded. It's using one's powers for good, like Samantha on *Bewitched* did.

I recommend *Creative Visualization* to anyone who needs to clear a log jam in their head. In a nutshell, it's about using positive words, ideas and images to attract positive things to your life. It works off the theory of "like attracts like." If we act "as if" something is already in our life, we can help make it a reality. Knowing that I could play an active part in what happened in my life was the most powerful thing I picked up from it.

I never felt like I had a firm, creative hand in my own life. I was a sailboat on a lake with no one at the helm, and I drifted wherever the wind took me. But with this little paperback, I began to feel like I was at the wheel.

> **The small shift of imagining the good that is possible in any situation turned out to be pretty seismic.**

The thing is, without getting too woo-woo and going too far down the rabbit hole, I do think our thoughts create things. Not that we can will a new car into our garage by just thinking about it, but I do think we ultimately shape and create our lives by what we think about. Peter McWilliams wrote the book *You Can't Afford the Luxury of a Negative Thought.* I haven't read it, but I love the title. If positive thinking can indeed help to bring about the things we want in life, then the idea of sabotaging it with negative thinking is heartbreaking.

> **Our negative thoughts can hold us back from everything we desire, including being thin.**

It can seem so unimaginable to only focus on the good and the positive, bright, light, and happy things in life. But I do think it's possible. It's not that we're whistling past the graveyard or ignoring the elephant in the room (sometimes nothing illustrates a point like a cliché). It's that we are leaning towards a more hopeful and positive perspective, rather than stewing in the stink of the past. It's about letting things go, like bad experiences and other people's hurtful statements we've clung onto. Once we do that, we can focus on what we want. We open up the space for our dreams and desires to plant themselves.

Thinking about the past—and then even worse, taking it as some sort of judgment of ourselves and prediction of the future—keeps us stuck. We get trapped in a loop, continuously repeating patterns of behavior from the past because we are repeating the negative thinking. And then we do not move forward.

I have moments when I catch myself beginning to spin the blender of negative thinking. I begin to bathe in: "Well, who do they think they are to say that? They are so rude and thoughtless and inconsiderate. Maybe I am a loser and clueless, blah, blah, blah." Then I will catch myself and think, "Wow, I don't need to take this on and try to make sense of it." I'm letting what someone said or did to me have all the say in how my day goes. Or, more likely, I'm spinning my own little narrative about what they said or did, and that's what's getting me stuck.

I can just move on to the next thought; I can think about what I want to think about. This is a beautiful moment when it happens and my spirit feels 10 pounds lighter.

I believe we can turn up the brightness of our thinking and make positive changes in our lives. Just saying it out loud feels like a shift. I begin to say I'm a fledgling at it, but I don't want to use that term because I think we all can—any of us—become an all-star at it right now, in this moment. This helps me: I will stop and and take note of something that is troubling me. It could be something said at work or as small as a cashier scolding me for not putting my shopping cart back. I will think, what is the most positive thing I could think about this? Usually what comes to mind is something that's also compassionate, like the other person was having a bad day. This might be what is referred to as our "higher self" at work.

I'll slip into old negative thinking for spells, but like emotional eating, my hope is each time is a little less. All I need is a reminder, and I am back on track.

**Note:** Reread the last few paragraphs as needed.

## A turning point

I began to walk again every night because it also helped with the negative thoughts that accumulated throughout the day. To settle down and clear my head and shift to a more open, positive place, I walked the streets of the city. I would walk faster and faster like I was running away from bad things in my mind. When I was at my mom's, I would walk the country gravel roads past fields of cows that stared at me like they knew my troubles and fields of corn stalks that seemed to wave at me when they blew in the wind. That's where I still felt most at home.

> **Walking catches the random good feelings we have and cements them in. Walking resets us to our original factory settings.**

Many, many nights, I had a certain new resolve to not overeat and it was like, where the heck did this come from? I think the creative visualization was making a cellular change and all the walking was clearing the grime from my head and heart.

Walking through the beautiful neighborhoods of Minneapolis and down the gravel roads at the farm, past all the golden fields of southern Minnesota, kept me very present. I was in the moment, and all the lovely imagery won out over chewing out the events of the day and running images of the past in my head like an ominous Powerpoint presentation. I was in meditation.

Meditation works. It's an inconvenient truth because sitting silent for even ten minutes is a lot to ask of most of us. Meditation is hard, but the gist of it can be brought to just about anything we do, like walking, folding laundry, weeding the garden, and washing the dishes. Life simply gets better when I walk, and it's the meditative quality, I think. And I am much more likely to do a meditative walk and keep it up in life than to "meditate" in the traditional sense.

**I was getting so sick and tired of feeling less than. My insecurities and all the second-guessing about everything I thought, said, or did were becoming as annoying as all the people who bugged me in life. That's a turning point when that happens. My walking meditations and *Creative Visualization* seemed to be clearing my mind of useless clutter.**

## Doctor Handsome delivers tough love

I finally had good insurance and was almost giddy about going to the doctor for practically free. Then he said the inevitable, "We need to talk about your weight." Damn, I forgot doctors bring up stuff like this.

**He was maybe the first person with any kind of authority to speak directly to me about my fat.**

He did it softly and directly, staring straight into my eyes, which of course, made me blush and my heart pound enough to feel it in my back teeth. He was a very handsome and sexy doctor, so it was like I was on *ER* and George Clooney saw me naked and was administering tough love. Even with the cuddly bedside manner, my heart curled up to protect itself, like a fuzzy wuzzy caterpillar when touched.

"Yeah, I know. OK," I said, like a shamed robot. I could have said: "You should have seen me ten years ago." But my blood pressure was very high on this visit, so he had reason to bring it up. Maybe it was because I went to Chi-Chis the night before for 10 p.m. happy hour with my roommate and had three margaritas with a salty rim and chips, catsupy salsa, cheese queso with a skin on it, and refried beans that looked like dog food.

"We can either put you on medication (like my mom and dad), or you can try to lose some weight. See in a month how things are going."

"Yes, yes. Can we do that?" I asked, even though the decision was mine.

A month later, there was no weight loss, so he put me on a pill, but I came back a month after that and had lost 10 pounds. "Good job," his funky nurse with cat-eyed glasses and vintage clothes told me.

"Eric, you lost ten pounds!" the sexy doctor announced when he walked in, like I was a really good boy. I behaved well and got an A from the teacher.

My blood pressure had dropped, too, and he took me off the meds. "Yah, we've got the kind of blood pressure that goes up and down with your weight," Mom had said to me, in between puffs of her ciggy.

## Food addiction is a family affair

I had lost 10 pounds, and I still drank margaritas and ate chips and had two bagels for breakfast, and sometimes another bagel for lunch, and Chinese food from the lunchroom, and leftover doughnuts whenever possible. Many weekends I visited Mom, and this was almost always a food fight from *Animal House*. Only at 28 can this happen, though in all fairness, I walked an hour every day, faithfully, and had many, many days when I didn't eat a box of doughnuts or go to happy hour.

Mom needed her food too, more than ever. It had been many years since Dad died, and her kitchen counters were a landfill of Doritos and Bugles and puff corn and Oreos. Schwan's home delivery filled the freezer with ice cream goodies like at the state fair. "Oh, I love the Schwan's man," she would tell me. "I keep the door unlocked, leave a check on the table, and he gives me what I want." It really did work like that. He even put the items in her freezer the size of a VW bug.

When I would visit, I will-powered through the first day, but by the second night, the dam broke, and I met my old pals in the kitchen for a party. It was like a kegger with beer and music thumping "Don't You Want Me Baby," followed by "Thriller," and I would break into the zombie dance, in synch with all my creamy, sweet, salty, and crunchy friends. We'd hang out and laugh and get crazy and sing Bruce Springsteen's "Glory Days." This was how I wanted to spend my Saturday nights at the time.

My mom always wanted me to go to church with her the next morning. Sunday morning was her Saturday night. There I sat in the rock-hard pew at the back of the big, old Lutheran church with my dried-out mouth from the salt and sugar the night before. The smell of Avon and Old Spice drifted into my nose, and the pipe organ, on slow speed, ground out what sounded like varying tones of the sound when you scrape your car on the curb.

**I envied all the folks who could trade an hour on Sunday morning for some peace of mind and a ticket to heaven. If you can do it, it's the deal of the century.**

Just like that, the Apostle's Creed, read in unison like zombie robots, snapped me back to my 12-year-old imaginations of being trapped underground after I die. I would always imagine myself lying there for eternity because I was fat, ate boogers, and looked at the boys in the PE showers.

Why could I not dial into above? Someone up there left the receiver off the hook, and I got the busy signal. I listened so closely to the words and tried so hard to soak up the minister's sermon. To me, The Lord's Prayer was like reading a chocolate chip cookie recipe, though not as exciting. I slipped back to my teen years when all my emotions were so thick and heavy, and how in the hell did I survive it? Everything in church is like it's underwater and not at all joyous.

A couple of old women asked me, "Do you still sing?" I would sing all the time in church during high school, not very well, but rather pseudo-opera. It was like I was trying to get the devil out and connect to something deeper and more spiritual; my singing was a mix of an old lady and a screechy angel. I would get away from them just before the marriage question came up. The organist had recently left because the Lutheran church accepted gay ministers. Another member hated rainbows because they are a gay symbol. Who hates rainbows? But I'd go with my mom to church because she asked, and I might as well have had a food hangover with a dry mouth and foggy head because nothing would sink in anyway.

Mom now rode a little cart around her house, and she wasn't supposed to. It was meant to be pushed. It was a rolling walker with handlebars like a bike, and a little cushioned seat that lifted up and had a little place for her to store her Kleenex and the bags of peanut butter M&Ms that were her happy pills. I think they were about all she ate.

When I visited, I'd cook up a storm thinking I could make food she would magically love, but trying to get someone to eat is as futile as trying to get someone to stop.

When we'd sit down to lunch, Mom would play the anorexic game. "I ate before you got here," and then she'd take a bite or two and push it around her plate. She would start to crawl backward like a crab on her little stool because she had taken to sitting on it at the kitchen table and everywhere. She scooted herself to the fridge to get herself an Equate. It was the Walmart version of Ensure, and she cracked it open like a cold beer.

I've tasted it. It's a very sweet, runny vanilla malt, and she sipped it with a little grin. I'm not sure if it was to say, "Look, I'm getting my vitamins and minerals, so it's fine I don't eat my lunch." Maybe it was more like, "Screw you, I can do anything I want, and you can't tell me what to do. I have the final say in this. No one can make me eat anything I don't want to." She would then roll some more, her little feet shuffling her along, and she would give that little, self-satisfied, defiant look even more.

I believe the egg bake in a cake pan I made was the one solid thing she did eat. I chopped many onions and mushrooms, sautéed them in a pool of oil, then added a dozen eggs and so much cheese. Mom somehow collected cheese like she was hoarding it, so I would empty whole bags of the shredded white and orange mix into the bake. She was eating nothing but this and Equate and peanut butter M&Ms. I thought if I could just pour everything I could into these eggs—everything I could give her to make her okay, including love—it would help. As I cooked, I would think lovely thoughts about life, infusing the egg bake like I was spitting into it.

I don't think Mom even wanted the food I cooked when I visited, but I think she thought that I wanted to cook for her. I had plastered on such a smiling face about it all, she perhaps thought it gave me something I needed. I had grown to be such a master at hiding my real feelings, and maybe I convinced her that I loved spending my Saturdays making food no one ate. But trying to figure out the workings of someone else's mind is a crossword puzzle where the letters keep changing. I do know food was our family loyalty, and it was the way she and I knew how to be together with love.

> **But I was beginning to see that my dependence on the approval of others was as strong as my dependence on food.**

Addiction to other's approval and food or booze are common companions. They both give the same momentary payoff of feeling everything is okay, but they combine to form a magnetic hole deep in the core of the gut, and this void is the size of a basketball.

One thing she would always finish was my French silk pie made in a southern Minnesota cake pan. This was Mom's make-life-tolerable pie. It's the one thing that seemed to truly excite her now that she had congestive heart failure and couldn't have her cigarettes, the true love of her life.

I understood her need for the big vat of caramel corn she once made in the oven, for sport, like some knit or play tennis. She popped the corn in oil on the stove top, boiled butter, and brown sugar until it's at the perfect thick, golden state, then dropped in a teaspoon of baking soda, and it bubbled up like Alka-Seltzer. She poured all this into the popcorn in a big roasting pan, swirled it around, tasted it, and then blissed out. It was a magic potion and a secret medicine for happiness and momentary peace of mind. After she baked it for an hour, it crunched, picked her up, and excited her. The pan of caramel corn delivered what life seemed to fail on.

## Creating our own reality

I remember one Saturday in July when I went out on a sailboat on a big Minnesota lake with four friends. We drank beers, got very chatty, peed in a bucket, and repeated the process many times. The sun was so warm and bright it purified the soul. Yes, there was a captain, a man who controlled the wheel, but even he fell into a sloppy kind of paradise fog. We were blissed out, like cows in the pasture slowly chewing on our cud, and then suddenly we heard, "Hey, hey, hey" and "Oh, shit," and the captain jerked loose from his relaxed pose. We were headed straight for another boat. He yanked us to the left just in time, and we skimmed by the other boat full of people giving us the finger.

So, the big question for me was how to get to that blissful state of detachment in life without the beers (and food) and with one hand on the wheel. That's the question for everyone. We are all in this together as we withstand and endure this earth state, this world society.

How do we fit into the community we've landed in, make our financial way in the world, and maybe even enjoy our time here?

**Perhaps the secret is to create our own reality.**

That's all there really is in life anyway. All we truly have is the reality we create in our own personal universe the size of our outstretched arms. It's our own personal reality; it's made up of our own laws and boundaries, as well as beautiful, soul-level things we love. Yes, there are world realities we need to face, like paying the bills and obeying laws and respecting others, but most of us have these things covered.

There really is no universal life code to crack and no marching orders to follow. There is no subscription to an all-encompassing life magazine that arrives in the mailbox to study and follow. I had always thought there was some overarching life skill to learn and master. But, in a word, no. Perhaps all there is to master is our own heart but sadly, we lose our connection to it.

I am responsible for my happiness. We all are. We don't need to be subject to the whims and edicts of others for this. But I've noticed that naysayers and skeptics will come out of the shadows when you begin to live by your own set of life happiness rules. The surprised and skeptical looks and remarks appear and often begin with, "You're doing what?"

What I needed most was to be comfortable being different in the world. I needed to lose my addiction to the approval of others and society as a whole.

Religion, education systems, and government entities, to name a few, have taught us to believe that everyone is better off when we all do as we are told. But that's not the case.

> **We make the world a better place for everyone when we are ourselves. It can be isolating or even embarrassing to follow the beat of your own drummer, but in the end, it feels so damned good and may be the only thing that saves us.**

One Sunday, I woke up under a dark cloud after being blown off by an opera singer I sort of dated. I was about to begin a day of feeling like shit because this guy didn't like me, plus I still suffered from general Sunday morning church PTSD. Then something just hit me.

> **I simply couldn't feel this way anymore, at least not today; the thought floated into my head from somewhere.**

It felt like I had finally figured out a math problem I struggled with. It was like my guardian angel lovingly slapped me on the face. It wasn't an Ike Turner slap, but more of a comic slap like Karen gives Jack on *Will and Grace*. It didn't sting but felt light and good.

I made an emotional U-turn in the middle of the road. I deliberately climbed out of my psychic hole and faked a good mood and enthusiasm for the day until it set in authentically, which it eventually did. More and more days started like this. They required deliberate effort at first, but more and more they happened naturally. The brighter mornings began to outweigh the darker ones.

It had been quite a while since I liked getting up in the morning. I hadn't felt that yummy Saturday morning/summer vacation burst of enthusiasm for the day in a long time. Junior and senior high and college had been rough. I was scared and anxious all the time, and daily doses of that ripened into plain old sadness. Since moving to Minneapolis, all the fear and worry metastasized into something bigger. A depression tumor grew for about five years. It was a benign tumor but still, it wreaked havoc.

**To feel crappy had become a habit, and I do think it was habit as much as anything.**

But the mornings became a happier time. Days could still hit the skids and circle the drain and eventually wash out to the Mississippi River, which is where everything, good and bad, ends up in Minneapolis. But no good came to me in a day when I got off to a pissy start, so I began to make a conscious choice to at least begin with a positive outlook poker face.

# Chapter 11

## Then Jazzercise step-ball-changed into my life

Two work friends and I were at Chi-Chi's happy hour one day. We crunched on corn chips, drank our fishbowl-sized margaritas, and commiserated about how much we wanted to lose weight. The healthy-life chat at happy hour soothes the general guilt of the fat, salt, sugar, and alcohol. If you talk about going on a diet or starting to work out, it cancels out all the bad in our heads.

My one friend had been the queen of aerobics in the 1980s. "We should try Jazzercise." She said the word, probably a little slurred and elongated, and it was like a movie moment when someone says something and the spotlight shines on them. A chord was struck. The word stuck in my ear like the song "Flashdance" did in its day.

The first time we went, we ate Bruegger's bagels before and went to Chi-Chi's for a late happy hour after. For the hour between, we moved as if at a disco or in the chorus of a Broadway musical. Honestly, I felt like I had arrived at the pearly gates at the entrance to the rest of my life. The best moments of my past met with hope for the future.

In Jazzercise, you dance to the original songs—no techo-pop covers—and you do routines that could be in a community theater musical. The grapevines and step ball changes and stutter steps and turns were much more involved than some of the musicals I'd been in. The routine to "Don't Go Breaking My Heart," the version with Elton John and RuPaul, would have worked in summer stock. We even danced to a funked-up dance mix from *Phantom of the Opera* with a move where we flailed a cape over our faces that were masked in our imaginations.

I escaped to another world during Jazzercise. I entered through a little stage door and became the professional dancer I knew I could have been. I tapped into the dormant kernel deep inside of me that could have been a dancer, but it never sprouted because of the fat and because it was southern Minnesota, far away from any dance schools. More so, I thought boys couldn't be dancers, and certainly not little fat ones. Girls do that. Fairies might be dancers, but I was so desperately afraid of being found out as one of those.

The thing is, I could have become a dancer, even at grad school age. I could have lost weight and tucked myself under the wing and tutelage of Lewis Whitlock at grad school, who thought I could really move. He saw something in me. Mankato even had a dance minor.

But here I was, and this was exciting. It was a fantasy realized. I would float to the ceiling and observe myself in the chorus of a Broadway musical. I experienced the euphoria when you are the type who connects to dance, and you are doing it. It was the easy, down-to-the-core good feeling that comes when you're doing something you love like nothing else.

**It was like everything inside turned into bright colors and began to swirl, and I dropped the sandbags, and like a hot-air balloon, I took off.**

I was the Wizard leaving Oz behind, and in my version, Oz was whatever bugged me from the day at work and years of accumulated psychic garbage. Nothing else mattered. I was in my body, but a million miles away.

The teacher would tell the class to bring it down a little, and I knew she was talking to me. It overcame me like nothing ever had and I would dance so hard and fast and rev up my heart to the point I felt an ache in my jaw. I would often catch her as she lost herself, too, as she left her reality with an extra skip and leap.

A cool-down song ended with the lyrics "the hero lies in you," and we would hug ourselves tight.

> **The assistant passed out frozen washcloths, and I would wipe my
> face, neck, and arms down like I was wiping off all the bad feelings
> and guilt and maybe even the melted fat.**

Fat from how many years ago? 20-year-old fat or more? I wiped off that
comment Dad made about being a sissy or the look the kids in kindergarten
gave me or the burnout who spat on my head in 7th grade or all the stares and
laughs in the shower in PE. Maybe even the guy who shoved the unwelcome
dildo up me on a date a year earlier got wiped off and discarded.

It all got cleared and thrown back in the pile of Jazzercise washcloths and
laundered and drained away. Then the cloths were taken out of the machine,
stacked, put in the freezer, and made clean and new and ready for the next
class, which for me, was always the next day. Anything that ends with a
refreshing frozen washcloth feels like a baptism.

Jazzercise spoke to a lost part of me. It reclaimed a chunk of my soul. This
is what exercise is all about. This connection makes people run around the
lake early in the morning, even when it's snowing. It's why power cyclists
look so determined and focused, like they're biking their way to salvation.

> **The secret to exercise is to find something that connects to a lost
> part of yourself and reclaims something left behind in life. The
> abandoned dancer or kid who loved to bike a summer day away.
> Then when you do it, you retrieve a part of yourself, and the feeling
> makes you soar. All you want is more. Walking does it for me, too.
> When I walk, I feel like an adventurer hiking to a higher plane in
> my own life.**

I Jazzercised with the commitment and gusto I usually reserved for food.
Exercise at this level was plain and simple, such a change for me, and change
jumpstarts your personal energy field. Any action does.

Then they installed a workout room at the phone company, and I'd sneak out early at lunchtime and ride the exercise bike for 60 minutes. It wasn't aggressive—about like Elvira Gulch riding her bike to get Toto after he bit her leg. I'd shower and be back at my desk just a little late. My boss was a good egg, a nice, big Wisconsin woman who knew I flirted with blood pressure issues. All the sales reps knew too, so no one minded me being off my desk for a long lunch. High blood pressure is a card you can play a lot to get your way.

Ah, the exercise bike. I have one sitting in my home office to this day, a few feet from my desk. It's a miracle piece of exercise equipment, especially the recumbent variety that is so easy on the body. An hour on the bike at the end of the day while reading or watching a favorite TV show is soothing and uplifting. It actually makes my trick knee feel better and also gets my heart rate up if I push myself.

Is it the most aggressive exercise? No, but I look so forward to the hour that I hate to miss it; regular moderate exercise is as good or better than sporadic intense workouts, I find. I bought mine for less than $150, and you can find them used everywhere. When I win the lottery, I will gift a recumbent exercise bike to everyone who needs to lose weight and exercise more.

Jazzercise, the exercise bike, walking (and gardening) have been my workout Yodas over the years. Finding something you love so much that you don't want to miss it is the secret. Anything else is futile and will be left behind.

## Filling the hole inside with vegetables

Most nights after Jazzercise, I stopped at the grocery store and picked up many little plastic bags of vegetables. I'd dump them all in a pot and cook them for supper.

**One healthy habit always prompts a second and then a third for me.**

The summer before Dad's heart exploded—the last summer Mom and Dad were both on the farm—they did the same, but theirs were from epic vegetable gardens they planted. They took over sections of the lawn and farm fields, turning them over with the big plow and then cultivating them by hand. They'd rake the black, southern Minnesota soil, like ground-up Oreo cookies, as smooth as the worn-down carpet in our living room. In went beets, celery, cauliflower, onions, kohlrabi, carrots, radishes, squash, potatoes, and many, many tomato plants.

They would steam a mix of all these until they were tender and then dump them in bowls with a pat of butter, lots of pepper, and a sprinkling of salt. They were so fresh that sometimes a little grit was still on them; it wasn't much, about like eating at the beach. The beets gave the whole batch a beautiful blush tone.

What a glorious way to eat. All anyone would need to do to be thin is garden on this scale and eat this way. Dad and Mom's big pots of vegetables planted themselves in me deeply.

Many nights I would cook potatoes, carrots, onions, green beans, peas, and corn in the very same pot they did. The colors were so vibrant all piled together, how could this vegetable kaleidoscope not be incredibly good for me? While they cooked, the kitchen smelled like digging in the earth, and the windows steamed up. I would doodle in the steam, a type of meditation and prayer, while I waited for them to soften to the mushy stage I preferred. Nearly baby food is what I love. The smoothness was soothing, and the grit from unwashed potatoes added a little texture for interest. Salt added flavor, and pepper added spice for entertainment. Butter added comfort, and even with the extra calories of the butter and starch of the potatoes and carrots, I could eat a mixing bowl the size of a hard hat and feel very full and lose weight.

> An enormous bowl of steamed vegetables is the dieter's best friend. To this day, when I need the comfort of shoveling it in to fill the big hole in there, this does it.

## Is that noticeable weight loss I see?

I'd ride a bike for an hour at noon and dance most evenings in a church basement. Many of those same nights, I ate a giant pot of steamed vegetables. One night while watching *Tales of the City* on PBS (yes, I remember it that specifically), I caught a glimpse of myself. My fat was no longer an inner tube around me. It had deflated and dropped. It looked like a bag of water sitting on a counter, the kind you bring a goldfish home from the pet store in. It also had the look of a fallen souffle and you might think how could I be happy about this, but I could see I was losing weight, and I felt like I had just won the Powerball.

The scale in the workout room had become my confession booth and oracle. I shared my sins, and it told me my future. It also determined how I would feel for the day. Scales have always done this for me because my weight is such a major part of my self-esteem. It just is.

It was a winter day so cold it made my car groan (again, I remember it that specifically). I slid the marker left and looked for the arm to lift and balance. It did that slow-motion and nerve-wracking bob, and at last, it settled. I looked. It was well below 240. Around 237. I weighed less than in eighth grade when Mr. Klunder announced my weight to the class like I was the winning hog at the state fair. I had lost over 40 pounds.

Christmas was looming and I went to Mom's house for a few days. This 237 number had me so pumped I never ate after 6 p.m. To not eat in the evening, especially during cookie and candy season at Mom's house, really was a Christmas miracle. It was as confounding as a virgin giving birth. How many of us have tried to figure that one out at Christmas Eve service?

I felt like I had left a big, heavy, winter coat of yesterdays and years past in a coat check room somewhere. I wondered, did the 40 pounds gone include the fat that was with me at 14, old and yellowed? Or were the fat cells all recently regenerated and getting spit out? These 40 pounds gone were a real shift in my body. It was like not carrying around ten big bags of potatoes.

I felt light, new, and honestly, all-around improved. And I felt hopeful.

I also felt accomplished. I had affected the change. I rode the bike, danced the steps, and ate the vegetables. I had begun to find a way to not always go to the negative and eat my feelings. Stay tuned for more on this. All this built self-confidence. I seemed to be cleaning house and sweeping away the mess left by everyone in high school. I was taking a hose to all dirt, mud, and shit the high school boys had tracked in and left on me. Dings on my psyche were fading. Nasty remarks made by theater teachers and directors, as well as random homophobes and other a-holes that roam the earth, were being left in the past where they belong. The pounds lost seemed to open up room for more positive thoughts and emotions to take over.

> **I needed weight loss success so much. Seeing the number drop is the only thing that has ever kept me going. This is so important for anyone trying to lose because we, the overweight, can't imagine the whole concept can work for us until we experience it. It's probably why all the diets and weight-loss plans you see out there seem to have a two-week start-up that's pretty strict.**

For the first time, I felt triumphant at something. It was becoming the most important thing in my life, more important than the random words or looks from others. When someone bugged or unnerved me, this sense of accomplishment kept me from an impulsive reach for food. Not always, but it often did.

Muscle memory is something dancers have; their muscles memorize a step or gesture and can repeat it without the mind needing to intervene. I had the muscle memory of eating. So much of it was simply a learned mechanical response. The dose of self-esteem from my success helped me to stop grabbing food impulsively. It gave me a new presence of mind that was there about 75% of the time.

## The scale became my new addiction

I began every day by grabbing and prodding and squeezing every inch of my body to assess my fat. Did last night's dancing burn up a pound? Did my overeating yesterday do damage? Please let me not have gained any weight, this was my morning prayer, and then I crawled down the basement stairs to where I stashed the scale to see if it was answered. I moved stealthily, like Gene Kelly in a dance routine. It was a habit I formed from growing up in a house with squeaky stairs and wanting to be generally anonymous. I sneak up and down stairs to this day to not make noise and bother anyone, even when I am home alone.

Once downstairs, I dropped my sweatpants and t-shirt. In front of me was the barometer of how my day would go. It had all the power to make it bright or shady, which is how I had always lived my life. The teachers, the other kids, Dad, the theater professors, stage directors, and my bosses—how they acted towards me is how I would feel about myself. That's what I looked to the scale for.

First, I reset it, which Mom taught me to do, to get it to zero. I'd tap, tap, tap with my toe, and then I grabbed the exposed rafter above and descended onto the square-foot platform. I lowered myself like a cow in a big harness. 239 was fine. Over and I had screwed up, and I'd scream at myself in my head. 237 or below was a success, and a good day was in store. I checked it over and over and over to see how I would feel.

Fast forward 30 years: The scale and I have gone to a couple's counseling of sorts, and we are in a healthier relationship. It took a while, but we have an agreement—I don't turn over my sense of self to him, and he keeps me honest about my eating. (I think of the scale as him because I really do have a sense that he is a living, breathing being in the house, and he's a man because I still fear men a little.)

I have periods when I don't weigh myself, and this is usually a period of denial about my eating. I think I can get by with downing a few tablespoons of soft cream cheese before bed. Eating free M&Ms at work is fine. Making numerous peanut butter and jelly sandwiches during the tricky 4 to 6 p.m. period is no problem. Finishing the tub of Cool Whip we had for my niece's birthday cake, if done in secret, has no effect.

Then one morning I will mysteriously think, I need to weight myself. It's time to face reality. I pull him (the scale) out from his home under the sink and step on gently so as not to upset him, and yes, I've usually gained about five pounds. First, I will curse and maybe even kick him a little (which he can take, he's used to it). I scream inside at myself, but not too loud or long. Then I thank him and listen to the reminder that his reading isn't personal; it's simply the science of weight gain.

A certain peace comes over me, and I begin the day with a new mindset. I accept that I am no longer 175, but 180, and this is simply the way it is.

> **Weighing myself in reasonable amounts, which for me is about three times a week, keeps me thin. Food addicts have a hard time seeing their bodies, and their eating, objectively. The scale is my honest friend who loves me but does not let me get away with crap.**

## If not food or the scale, then where do I get my self-esteem?

What if the whole self-esteem and self-confidence and self-love thing isn't the mystery I'd always thought it was? Some people seem to be born with heaps of it. Some seem to grow up in families with a mom with a self-worth magic wand she waved around like the fairy godmother in Cinderella, and poof, everyone felt like a million bucks. All through school, I thought the bullies had it, but they don't. Bullies have less of it than anyone.

Then there were all those perfect theater kids in college and around the theater community who could walk into an audition room and just own it.

They flirt and make it seem like they are best friends instantly with everyone. They're thin and pretty, their clothes fit perfectly, their words flow out of their mouths on waves of butterscotch sound, and they always know what to do with their hands. Was their self-confidence really all that solid or maybe all illusion?

If the scale isn't telling me I'm a good boy and have done well, who is? If I don't go to food when I feel unsafe, insecure, bored, or generally not in control, then what do I do?

Do I try to not to give such a damn? One day it struck me, that's what I needed to do. I simply must not give such a damn about what others think or say.

> **Getting over the real addiction of caring so much about the opinion and approval of others might be what it's all about. It helps to do things that make us feel good about ourselves—even real little things—and do them every day, over and over. Bit by bit, we'll care more about what we think of ourselves versus what others think of us.**

How odd that it can be so hard to do this at first, but it gets easier. More on this later.

I would have been so disheartened to know how long it would take me to discover the act of doing small things daily to make myself feel good. I had been waiting so long for the magic fairy dust from somewhere or someone to land on me, but like Dorothy in *The Wizard of Oz*, I always had the power.

# Chapter 12

## The body

For two decades, I belonged to a mix of LA Fitness, the YMCA, and the YWCA; something positive besides exercise comes from working out at a gym. It's a community of the like-minded. I barely spoke to anyone, but I surrounded myself with people who, I imagine, were either trying to lose weight or stave off the effects of last night's excesses like I often was. Most were not especially thin or fit, but there were very few who were obese. It's like the end result of many who are working out is not getting huge. If we eat whatever we want but also exercise, people don't seem to get too big.

You can study other bodies at the gym, which is helpful if you've never had a normal body. Guys look at other guys' bodies all the time. Men are as obsessed with their looks as women and are probably more insecure about them as a whole.

Bodies of fit 20- and 30-somethings are of minimal interest to me. To see what a man's body can be at 50, 60, 70, and 80 is encouraging. I'm inspired by the 60-something man who has a fit body with just a gentle expansion of the stomach, and looks like he's been doing cardio and lifting weights for years. I'm guessing he knows he can't eat all evening and splurge all weekend, like he may have been able to in his 20s and 30s. Sunday Funday is a thing of the past.

I can tell most of the men never had an obese body like I did. Even if they have a belly, the rest is usually pretty fit; they look 55 from the front and 35 from the back.

I've never had a good body. I'm not like most men who can look back to high school or their 20s and say, "Damn, I was hot." I went from one of *The Far Side* kids to very overweight to having a body that is the remnants of having once been 380.

I carried hundreds of extra pounds of fat at my heaviest. Until I got to about 265, I pictured a magically muscled and fit body under it all. I remember this art toy that was around in the late 70s where you chipped and picked away at a block of something that looked like plaster of Paris, and suddenly a statue of David appeared. As a youngin', that's how I thought it would go. It was at least hopeful.

The first male bodies I saw were in this scary book, *Religions of the World*, that lived in the bottom of a stack of magazines on a shelf in our dining room. I would drag it out, and it shook my little world. I stared endlessly at all the Michelangelo paintings of the condemned sinners and flying nude men with confusingly small penises, but very sculpted, muscled bodies. They weren't working out in the weight room the wrestlers used. That must be my body's natural state, I thought, under all the flab, but I was discovering this is not the case.

Then there is the whole thing about my particular body. I didn't have one of those fat bodies that looked kind of sexy, like Seth Rogen. I always looked like I should be thinner. A lot of big guys have their fat under their muscles, so they have a ripped kind of beefcake fat. I had lumpy, loose, bumpy, flabby fat right under the skin. Imagine holding a mesh bag of semi-rotting onions. Plus, I have that unfortunate male pear shape that is never as easy for a man to sport as belly weight. If you have big shoulders, you can carry extra weight better. I just wasn't an attractive fatty.

But I was now at the point where I looked pretty good with clothes on. The scary body stuff, the leftovers of 150 pounds lost, could be covered with clothes.

# Overweight people are all around

Fat people are everywhere, so I know I am far from alone with my food obsession. I consider myself forever a member of the fat kid's club, and all around, I see varying degrees of us, from slightly overweight to pretty big to obese to morbidly obese to enormous. I see it at work, with friends and family, at Target, at gas stations, and at the grocery store. I see the angst on someone's face when they're not feeling good about their body, when they're not at home in their own skin. They dress in drapey tops and giant sweatpants, like I wore and still do, and they pull a lot at their shirt and constantly stretch out their waistband.

I also see the sparkle that comes when the weight is lost.

> **Losing weight, enough to see and feel it, is such a dang good feeling.**

It feels great to have done something specific and difficult—to have first planned the weight loss and then mustered up the courage and dedication to finally get the wheels turning. It feels like winning the lottery because even though the science of weight loss is pretty clear, getting it to happen still feels like a lot of luck and a divine something at work. But five pounds lost is enough to prove to yourself it can happen, and you can lose five pounds with some pretty minor changes like not eating after supper for a couple weeks or starting to walk every night.

# What finally gets us started?

Weight loss of any amount, but certainly a big one, is life-changing. We all imagine and dream of it, but until we experience it we have no idea the impact. And until we lose some weight we doubt it can be ours.

When frustration builds up enough, that might get us to make a change, because the weight just wears on a person after a while. In a word, it's annoying. Nothing anyone ever said to me about my weight got me to do anything about it; remarks about my fat only made me eat more.

All the health risks don't seem to make a difference in motivating us. They tend to just make us feel bad and guilty for what we are doing to ourselves. The "revenge body" or wanting to look great at a daughter's wedding or a beach vacation have a better chance of getting us started. It's like the motivation has to somehow come from within. It has to be our idea.

Only an internal click of some kind will make the change and have a lasting impact; for me it was a series of clicks. I first had a flash that losing weight could make me feel better about myself. Then I had moments after I lost some weight where I could see that life got easier. When I started focusing more on my own opinions of myself, rather than those of others, taking care of myself just started to be easier and more natural, and even felt good, but this part was just beginning to dawn on me.

No one thing was the starter pistol going off for me. One by one, I began doing various "weight loss" things like walking, Jazzercise, eating mega servings of vegetables, and drinking fake sweet tea at night instead of eating.

My weight loss was a result of a series of relatively small things. As change happened, I got so excited I was inspired to keep going. Every time I lost a few pounds I got more hopeful, which kept me working at it.

> **When you get to the point of some success, the success is so motivating you continue, but a couple of weeks of blind faith is necessary to get started.**

Mine was a slower journey than it needed to be, but emotional eating was my constant companion; dieting as a compulsive eater was like going on a power walk with someone who just wants to stroll. For many of us, dare I say most of us, emotional eating is the culprit.

Getting to the core of my emotional eating was, and is, the most important thing of all, especially when it comes to maintaining my loss. Losing some weight, however you do it, needs to happen first though; getting to the heart of the matter is easier with some weight loss hope and confidence in your arsenal.

I think that is the thing to focus on—finding a way to just lose some weight. The terms blind faith and white knuckling come to mind. Perhaps you need to cloister yourself for a little while to keep away from the judgmental eyes of others. I've done this. Avoiding some people may be what's called for to get started. There were many times I needed to enter a self-created hermitage of sorts to focus on losing weight. People in their first year of sobriety—of any kind—are often counseled to do what they need to do make their lives as low-stress as possible. I think this is a brilliant plan; why can't it be a plan for the rest of our lives?

A few months into weight loss, a recommitment also needs to happen. I tend to get lax and a little pompous even. I begin to graze at night or pop candy in my mouth at work. A mental refresh of motivation is a constant and necessary thing along the way, especially when goals are achieved. Losing is thrilling. Maintaining is mundane.

> **You just want to be normal and eat without thinking, but most of us fat kids can't do that. Mindful eating will always need to be a part of our lives.**

TV commercials of joyous thin people touting their recent big weight loss with the help of a certain program play all day, every day. I'm always happy for them. Then I think, okay, let's chat in a year or two. From my experience, constant rededication is necessary when you're an emotional eater. Beach vacations, family weddings and special events where I wanted to rock a skinny suit, for example, have all reenergized me. They've all prompted me to lose the ten pounds I often gain over the holidays. These recommitments are necessary along the way.

Bottom line, as someone who lost 200 pounds and has kept it off for 20 years and counting, I want you to know, the change is thrilling, and life is better and more manageable with weight loss.

**Weight loss solves problems. Not all of them, but even the unsolved ones are easier to deal with.**

And the weight loss journey for an emotional eater is a life-long one, with many basecamps along the way where you need to stop, recommit, and reenergize.

## Get a hobby

I began a garden at the house I bought in the city. It felt like a return to my growing-up days of digging, planting, and picking on the farm. I began to dig again in hopes of finding something missing in myself; perhaps it was something good I left on the farm where there were genuinely beautiful and happy periods. Thirty-some years later, these moments outshine the awful ones that were, in truth, done at the hands of only half-a-dozen or so local bullies. It wasn't the whole town or world like I had in my head. I wasn't a fat and faggy Frankenstein being chased out of the village by the townspeople.

Gardening is a lot like Jazzercise to me. I lose track of time during it, and food rarely enters my mind. This is a Godzilla-sized feat. When I am in the middle of it, I prefer it to eating chocolate chip cookies on the couch. I feel all-around better down to the core when I do it. I feel grounded and whole.

Gardening saved my life. I've had many St. Francis of Assisi moments when I've thrown my arms into the air and thanked God (which was still just a word to me in my 20s and 30s) out loud for gardening in my life. It's one of the main things responsible for my losing weight, and it's in the top three things that keep it off.

It's the physicality of it, for sure; when I garden, I throw myself into it. But it's so much more than that. It's also the emotional balm it provides. When I work in the garden, it's like I leave my troubles in the dirt where Mother Nature handles them. Plus, it simply gets my mind off food. Could it be that gardening and other hobbies show us what is most important in life, at least in our own corner of the world?

The eating and the exercise are the science of weight loss. To drive the garden analogy home, they are the nutrients, the water, and the sun.

> **But everything else inside that makes us go to the food and get fat, that's what matters most. I think what is often missing when our addictions take the wheel is a connection to a purpose and a lack of what makes our soul and spirit sing.**

Hobbies restore that connection. My heaviest years were the years I didn't garden. The more I gardened, the thinner I got.

Gardening is my #1 hobby, and cultivating hobbies might be the most life-changing and life-saving thing we can do for ourselves. My mom was a master at it.

One definition of a hobby is favorite occupation. Hobbies say who we are at our core. They make us happy, and it sounds just too sunny to be true, but I think that's what life is about—cultivating happiness from things we love to do. Helping others is a necessary and enriching part of life, but I think it's the things we do for ourselves that make us happiest... like hobbies.

> **Hobbies are a higher calling that bring us meaning and purpose. They show us what we would do all day if we could, and what reveals the core of our being more than that? Nothing can get us in touch with ourselves like a hobby.**

Working on a project daily and making it more beautiful and complete builds self-esteem. It's powerful to effect a positive change on something and make the world—even your tiny part of it—better. Gardening, knitting, painting, pickleball, biking, cooking, macrame, antiques... the list is endless. We all have a couple. I don't accept when someone says they don't have one, but it may have been abandoned somewhere in the past.

> **I know that many times when I head to the kitchen, if I stop and think about it, I'm just bored.**

I'm skimming over the surface of my day, afraid to drop into something deeper, and too many moments like this turn into days and then weeks and then a life that is unexplored and unrealized and often, addicted and overweight. When I see someone without at least one hobby, I think something is missing in their life. I also think hobbies are meant to be somewhat obsessive, and I have found the deeper I dive into my hobbies, the less I need food.

## The fat realist approach

I had always thought losing weight meant intense restriction. Perfectly modest amounts of only low-calorie foods was the dieting maxim I needed to follow. But no matter how I tried, it was like shoving my size 11 foot into a size 9 shoe.

I decided to strike up an agreement with food. I finally admitted my food addiction might never completely leave and keeping food in my life—even in a big way sometimes—was the way to go. I faced the truth that food would never play second chair in my life. I became a functioning food addict. This one shift in thinking was the only way I could lose the rest of my weight and keep it off.

I accepted my food dependence and figured out how I could still be addicted to it but make it a friendlier, less damaging dependence.

> **Sometimes I simply need to eat and eat and eat. After decades of fighting it and feeling shame and guilt and remorse, I realized it's a fiber in the fabric of my being. It just isn't going to go away completely, so the most practical approach is to incorporate it**

**into my life in the least harmful way.**

When I worked at a non-profit that served people experiencing homelessness, they used the term harm-reduction. If someone couldn't be completely sober, waiting until noon to drink was a step forward. It wasn't the model of sobriety, but it was so much better than being loaded 24/7.

**I may always need to eat big at certain times in my life. I settled into this thought, and it was a giant exhale. This is the fat realist approach I began to accept.**

The perfect dieter's deprivation mindset always got me in trouble, and it still can if I don't check myself. Might I say, this perfection is what I observe when I see people lose and then gain it back. Who among us can sip water, breathe deeply, meditate, then eat moderately every time the emotional eating itch needs to be scratched? Some may. I can't, though sometimes I do. I began to accept this. Feeding myself multiple apples instead of doughnuts or half a watermelon rather than half a cake is sustainable to me.

Soon I was 220 pounds.

## Feeling this new 220-pound number

I have tell-tale spots where I can see and feel weight loss (and gain), like my lower back, my upper belly, and the sides of my face. I'd gaze into the mirror to look for my cheeks to cave in a bit and the bones to punch out. I groped my back and front to feel what less of me felt like.

I hovered under 220. That's the weight where my body really changed. Photos are the only reliable way to see my weight loss; I can't see it by looking in the mirror. I was getting to the point of looking like a typical 30-something gay boy. I was maybe even attractive, which takes a lot to write, but not as tough as saying it out loud. I was modestly handsome. I wasn't hot or cute, but good-looking, as my Grandma always called some men in town, and I usually agreed with her. I was also photogenic. I looked better in photos than in person.

There is such magic and power to being even a little good-looking when you have never been considered close to it. Fat just wasn't attractive back in the 80s and 90s. Now people seem to rock it. There are guys that if their fat is done right—under the muscle and it's less than, oh, 40 extra pounds—they are lumberjacks. There were no cute fat boys in the 70s and 80s. There was a 90s social group in Minneapolis of gay, fat guys, and they would have little ads in the local gay newspaper I sat and studied. This is where I could find a boyfriend, I thought, but wouldn't they kick me out if they discovered that my deepest desire was to be nothing like them?

I now looked normal, which is the term I used at the time, because normal was still what I wanted to be, maybe more than anything else. I think the normal ideal was a leftover from being a spectacle in my school growing up. But normal is such a mind-numbing, soul crushing term.

**I really didn't want to be normal, I wanted to be who I really was and not have to feel ashamed about it or scared of getting laughed at or beat up.**

So, I challenged myself to be not-normal. I even had moments of ballsiness.

I was driving through Uptown in Minneapolis, coming from Opitz Outlet, where I likely had purchased bags of 70% off clothes and sexy underwear to fit my new frame. I may have had a Calvin Klein jockstrap in one of the bags. I buzzed after these outings, plus coffee shops were popping up everywhere, so I'm sure I had a French roast in my cup holder.

I had the good caffeine buzz, the type that feels like you just got really good news. It's a buzz similar to half a glass of wine—happy, not sloppy or manic—and I felt like a sexy Minnesota surfer guy at the Minneapolis version of one of the cool Ventura Beach intersections you see on TV shows. I was stopped at the light where all the runners cross, and the perfect late-20s gay boy crossed in front of my truck and though I couldn't smell him, I knew how he smelled—like fresh air and Paco Rabanne. He was the kind of guy who leaves a bathroom smelling better than when he went in. He wore electric blue Nikes with no socks and biking shorts that revealed the shape of everything. He was shirtless with a smooth chest like a dune of sand and a flip of hair over his forehead. He was all three of the guys from *Friends* rolled into one.

I beeped my horn and flashed him a thumbs up with soap opera eyes and a head nod that I hoped said, "Oh, hell, yeah." I looked great from the chest up. He couldn't see the extra 40 pounds piled on the seats like potatoes. I pulled away, and he gave me a little wave, and in my head, I circled back and picked him up in my truck, and we went back to his place and made a porno. But I kept driving, and I felt as good as if we had.

Maybe the trip on the hottest afternoon I remember to the nude beach west of Minneapolis was the best body therapy I could do. It was the kind of day when you just can't cool down and I've chosen to never complain about the weather and that could be a farm kid thing. The weather gods could be offended, so I never do.

A friend had been to this beach with her hippie sister and described it as full of the kind people who bring sandwiches for others. I parked in a lot that was like a field approach on the farm and then I walked the gravel road to the beach.

Once settled in, I made my way into the water. Walking away from the crowd was fairly easy. I didn't have to see people's reactions when they spotted my ass that I thought was big enough to show a movie on.

I floated for about an hour on my back staring at the sky and letting the sun bleach the feelings of shame about my naked body out of me. I started to get a feeling of normalcy and no-big-dealness and I stood up and began to walk out slowly. I got full frontal before 75 or so other naked people. I presented myself like a girl coming down a spiral staircase at her coming out party in an old movie, but I wasn't presenting something big and special; I presented myself naked and normal and fine and just like everyone else. They didn't laugh, point or even notice, which was just what I needed.

The little kid who came up to me and smiled and reached out his hand forced me to stand there just a little bit longer, which was good. I wish I could have been as free in my naked body as the little six-year-old and he might have been trying to tell me to just not worry about it so much and maybe even, don't worry about anything so much. I wanted to be more like him, and I think six was when I started caring so much what others thought.

## Being thin is simply the best

Of course, I obsessed over getting thin. I had a lifetime of imagining all my problems would evaporate if I was skinny.

> **The reality is a lot of my troubles did go away. Not all of them, but I could see that life gets so much easier when you're thin.**

I had lost about 160 pounds, and I had a taste for what comes with it. Even at 220, I had moments of how great it feels to not be overweight.

Fat walks into the room first and demands everyone's attention. It announces you like a doorman, and in my head, it said, "Here comes the great big, sissy fat guy." Plus, it requires your attention before anything else. Fat is like flying on an airplane with a screaming toddler. Will I break that chair? Will I fit in that rollercoaster? Will I be able to find a shirt to fit me when everyone at work needs to wear a uniform? Thoughts like these were always spinning in my head.

A few of the glorious things: To no longer get the stares everywhere and the fearful looks from people when you board the plane. I know large people who have bought two airline tickets. No more giggles and smart-aleck remarks from little kids who must have parents who feel the same. Not fearing the breaking of chairs or beds. I bent the frame of my sophomore roommate's bed beyond salvage, as well as my cousin's bed when I was 12. No more thighs chafing to the point of blistering. Being able to find clothes anywhere that fit, though big clothes seem more mainstream now than in the twentieth century. No more constant pulling at my shirt to hide my boobs. No moisture strip left on plastic chairs, which is never spoken of, and so embarrassing. No panicking in line for rides at Disneyworld. I remember standing in the queue for Space Mountain with an enormous co-worker on one of those corporate reward trips in the 90s. He was in a jittery panic about whether he would fit once we got up to our little rocket. He fit, barely, and thank God because the embarrassment of being turned away with hundreds of people watching is epic. No more gentle sitting in the movie theater to test the strength of the seat. I broke one of those, too. The list goes on.

> **There's a freedom, an ease, a peace of mind that comes when the extra weight is gone. It's just so damned good. I'd love all overweight people to experience it, especially those who have always been fat, because you just can't imagine it when it's all you've ever known. I want to shake them and scream it in their ears and etch it in their brains somehow. Life gets so much easier.**

In addition to all the internal feel-goods, I also got all the compliments, and attention, and kudos, which is catnip. It was a bug that bit, and because I scratched, it got itchier. The positive attention became my new weight loss gasoline, which is tricky. If I was no longer going to look to others for validation I was okay, how can I get the good feelings from the remarks on my weight loss? But I did get the good feelings, plain and simple. It's a quandary that would sort itself out, but I do think the positive comments were sinking into my core and shifting my own opinion of myself to a brighter place. All the praise was a sort of mirror held up to me where I could start to see myself in a better light.

# Chapter 13

## Shoulding all over the place

I've done so much in my life based on "getting it right." So much time has been spent on doing the thing that will make the parent, the boyfriend, the boss, the teacher, the theater director, the editor, the creative director, and even the grocery store clerk say, "That's it, you've got it right. You are good."

Then I'd keep on trying to get it right, and that's such a pressure-filled and quite unsatisfying way to go about your day I'd often dread everything I needed to do. From writing a paper to getting my oil changed, I'd get a sick stomach and wait to get yelled at. Then came the wave of feeling like a big, fat disappointment, which was how I thought of much of my whole life up to this point.

> **Of course, we all have things we have to do that we don't always want to. Stepping out of our comfort zone is often how we grow and life on earth dictates some shoulds. But how often do we keep things in our lives we don't want just because they've always been there or we think they should be?**

So many of us get caught living lives of "should." We spend our days "deep in the should." This is how I was feeling at my job at the phone company and living in a city that didn't feel like home. I should like a job at a big company.

I should like to do something that makes lots of money. I should move to the city and take on big-town life. I should get a Master's degree. I should like having kids. I should like to live in a nice house in a nice suburb with a nice car.

I had a tendency to invite things into my life that made me uncomfortable, nervous, or generally not excited. I seemed to always have an excess of "shoulds" hanging around, and again, we all have some necessary ones, though I think just about anything can be questioned. Bad feelings about something or someone are almost always a red flag that something needs to go away, I think, but I didn't yet trust my feelings, my inner compass. This question became a turning point: What things just didn't fit into my life any longer? Or ever did?

## Filling the hole

I thought I needed to keep trying to do theater because it's all I'd ever known in my life, even though I always felt so uncomfortable and awkward on stage. The praise kept me hooked, but the nasty comments of professors and directors (usually straight males) killed the joy. I dreamed of being a star, which was, quite honestly, unrealistic. I was beating a dead horse, as that awful phrase goes. I was still hoping for the life affirmation that I was something special, which I needed so desperately.

> **This might be the cause of a lot of shoulds in life: Trying hard to fill the expectation of someone out there or society in general and proving that we are enough.**

It reminds me of when I squeezed into skinny jeans for a vacation to look cool and was so uncomfortable. I got stomach cramps and chafed my inner thighs raw.

This is also where addiction can creep in, and we are all addicted to something. I see it all around because it takes one to know one. It's food or booze or overworking or exercise or shopping or bitchy control or rage-filled outbursts or obsessive cleaning or worry. Being too nice or too helpful are really common ones, too. The list goes on. Whatever eases our uneasiness and gives us a little sense of control.

There's a hole that many of us feel deep down inside that we try to fill. The hole reminds me of this sinkhole I saw on the news one spring when potholes form everywhere in the streets and highways of Minnesota. People thought it was just a little pothole, and then boom, one day it opened up, and it was a cave in the belly of this intersection that a car landed in. Potholes are everywhere, but we laypeople don't really know what causes them, which is how I felt at the time about the hole inside me.

**I could feel the hole, but I didn't know what it was all about. I did know I never ever felt safe or good enough.**

Living the life of "should" expands and deepens the hole even more, and it will never be filled by living the life that perpetuates it. You can never get enough of what you don't want, as they say. We addicts will keep at it like soldiers, though.

If we are so out of touch with who we really are, like deep down at the creamy center, addiction takes off. If we know what our true colors are, but they seem not right or appropriate or what society expects or what will make our parents happy, then we seek something that will mimic genuine good feelings. But the fake feelings fade and then we feel so out of touch with the world, and mostly with ourselves.

**Addictions make us feel normal, like we fit in, by easing the discomfort.**

It's like little random mold spores at first, but addictions grow until everything inside is black and wet. Addiction is this creeping, invasive vine I run into all the time in the garden. As I try to pull, it's everywhere and wound around everything, and it's impossible to find where it sprouted. Maybe I do find the root, but I can tell that a little bit is still down in there. You can deny it, but it'll sprout again. It's only a matter of time.

I used to think that finding out what created this hole is the #1 task for the emotional eating food addict, but I've changed my mind. We don't have the time. I'd rather we spend it finding things that fill us up, besides food, and also getting the weight loss started because once we've lost some weight, everything gets clearer and easier to manage.

I had flashes at the time of the following idea, and I've now come to see it as truth: I need to do whatever it is I want to do in life. That's it. It sounds so simplistic and rather impossible, but I swear, it's the only way. We must do exactly what we want as best as we can. Note: we must also be responsible and kind and not do drugs or drink too much alcohol or constantly overeat or be mean to people, but beyond that, the choice is ours. To commit to doing what we want to do in life can feel defiant and wrong and privileged and lonely and even lazy, but whoever is way up there in the sky past the clouds, they smile when they see us do it. I can feel it. When I let myself do what I want, I don't need my addictive substances nearly as much; I have an incredibly easier time saying no to them. And I am a much better friend, husband, brother, uncle, neighbor, co-worker, and citizen of the world. I am happier, kinder, and easier to be around.

> **To do whatever we want to do, and do it responsibly and kindly, is the only way to escape an unhappy and addicted existence.**

I see it as especially crucial if you're a male in Minnesota. At least in my personal orbit, there's an epidemic of addiction and early death in us northern men, and I suspect it's the case in many places. To do what you want is the only way to avoid an early death or at the very least, to avoid dying inside while you're still walking the earth.

## Hiding one's food compulsion while dating

When you begin to date someone in earnest, you go out for breakfast with pancakes and sausages a lot, and then long lunches, and then drinks and dinner and late night happy hours, and then you start all over the next day. When my hubby and I started to see each other, we went to Starbucks many nights for a coffee, and he'd always ask, "Would you like a scone or something sweet?" I followed his lead, of course. I wasn't going to say, "Oh, I don't eat treats in public. I pick them up en masse' at Cub Foods and take them home and eat them in a ritual."

When we were getting to know each other, I didn't want to lead with: "Yeah, I'm obsessed with what I eat, which might make you think I don't eat much, but I eat so much, and I binge secretly, and even though I don't binge and puke anymore, that could come back at any time, because it's a great stress reliever. And every time we go out and eat lots of Chinese food, and get dessert and drink too much, and then get nachos, I feel so guilty and obsess about it, and that's why at 32, I'm getting the two frown lines between my eyes that look like the number 11. The lines down the side of my face, like a ventriloquist dummy, are from years of forced smiling. 'Like me, be nice to me.'"

You keep all that stuff to yourself. You can't diet your way through dating unless you meet at a Weight Watchers meeting.

This sounds like I'm being so hard on myself as I write this, but it's a reflection of how hard I was on myself at the time.

> **I wish I could go back and tell myself it was going to be okay. I'd say, "You are doing so well, Eric." I'd tell my 30-something self, "You are fine just the way you are. Enjoy the moment."**

If only I could have drunk that in with the fervor I soaked up sweet white wine and the ardor I took on a plate of nachos.

But hubby and I seemed to have a soul contract that connected us; no matter how hard it was for both of us to be in a relationship in the early days, we toughed it out. There we were: two gay men who grew up in the 70s and

80s and 90s and had similar battle scars. The same secrets were lodged in our throats. Tactics for getting through an upbringing of being different infused our personalities. We both had ways of dealing with the shame and guilt of disappointing our parents and society in general. Hiding the parts of ourselves we didn't like was one way we did this.

**Eventually, we discovered we were both food addicts, and nothing bonds two people like the need to eat.**

We addicts tend to find one another and we both made love to our food, kissing it like we were trying to get to second base. When we ate a great dinner, it was like being in a threesome. The tempura appetizer platter was like bringing Brad Pitt home to be our plaything for the night.

Not long after we met and much too soon, he moved in, and one day I came home, and there were potato chips on top of the fridge. An honest-to-God bag of Old Dutch Sour Cream and Onion potato chips with the top crinkled shut. I could do this, I thought with fresh optimism. "What should we have for lunch?" he asked. "I picked up some turkey for sandwiches."

I put a handful of chips on my plate and went into the living room where we sat and ate. I tried to eat like a normal person, but chips are like crack to me, and I felt a little creature come alive inside. It was a little gremlin that starts eating the chips, and needs more and more, and starts scratching at my core, like a dog at the back door wanting to get in.

Ten minutes later, I'm in the kitchen trying to be as silent as possible, though likely not silent at all. I picked up the art of the sneak from Mom in the womb and the belief that we are doing it without anyone knowing. I undid the bag of chips to get some more to feed Angus, as I called this thing that lives in me. Giving him a name helps; I had an actual something to try to reason with. But Angus always wins. You can't reason with Angus.

A few minutes later I'm back in the bag yet again, because Angus is relentless, and now-hubby walks in, and I get all smiley and giggly. "These are just so yummy I needed a few more."

Getting close to someone scared the shit out of me, so I tried to present my best self, and who can blame someone for this? I had plenty of good to share. The less good stuff? Well, we all have our shit. I'll play those cards later, I thought.

# IV

## Part Four

**PEOPLE PLEASING:**
*It's all been building up to this*

# Chapter 14

I have this constant thought, almost a mental affliction, that I need to work so frickin' hard to first feel the right thing and then say the right thing in just about any circumstance. I have it in my head that there is one right or one wrong way to think on most subjects and to feel in any situation. If I don't get it right, then I am dumb and clueless, and I feel bad about myself.

A long-ago co-worker said to me: "You take every comment or critique as a personal attack." I do.

> **If I could swipe one thing out of my life, it would be taking things so personally. It makes most interactions hurtful and life all-around harder.**

I wish my head could be like an Etch-A-Sketch toy, and when it's all scribbled full of this craziness, I shake it upside down, and it's clear.

Dad and I were perhaps so much alike in this—two incredibly sensitive types who had a hard time navigating the world. Not only did I inherit this from him, but we made it worse in each other. We each felt bad about what the other said or didn't say, and then we sulked, and then the other felt bad about that, and then we both read a lot into it. We lived in constant judgment and rejection of each other.

When someone says a certain thing to me, my gears lock up. My psyche grinds tight, and my stomach hardens and forms an armor plate. It's a moment of insane thinking, and I am that poor little animal that is cornered, and his fangs come out, and his claws start scratching, and why the hell do I think everyone is against me? It's a hangover from high school days that I just can't shake. It's also a survival tactic that we all have hanging around from caveman days and I think mine got jacked up even more as a teen.

The world is a tough place for sensitive, creative, and artistic types. And independent thinkers. It just is. Historically, it's probably the easiest it's ever been, but we still live in a world where one struggles when they feel "different."

Many of us crave a life lived in technicolor, and a sense of abandon, but doors seem to slam shut like someone put out a press release that reads: You can't live that unorthodox of a life. Get back to a normal existence. Make a damned living and dress like an ordinary person and settle down. This sounds like such a drab and cloistered existence it's horrifying.

> **For me, eating relieves the tension between who I am, who I want to be, and who I think the world expects. When I eat, I drift into a dreamy state that eases the strain.**

Eating temporarily corrects a seeming electrical short, a misfire in my head that I landed on the wrong planet. Food soothes, but then the regret sets in so quickly. As the pounds pile on, I feel even less okay. I need more food, and the cycle is endless.

> **My real addiction might be the endless pursuit to feel okay in the world.**

Yes, I know I am sensitive, very sensitive, overly sensitive. But what the hell do I do about it? Sometimes it makes me feel like I should crawl into a hole and call it a day and be a modern-day Emily Dickinson.

Or I could say to everyone, "I just don't care. What you say or think about me does not hold more weight than what I say or think about myself. Actually, it holds almost no weight." This is the answer, but wow, it can seem impossible to get there.

I have a very sticky energy field. Other people's thoughts, words, and deeds stick with me, like when our long-haired dog on the farm got into the cockleburs. He had them in his fur forever.

> **Every sense of anything about myself seems to be based on the approval of others. I think I need it to survive. If they don't like me, they can get rid of me.**

When someone says something like, "Hey, can you not leave dishes in the sink?" or "You forgot to send that email," I am shattered. I feel scolded and ashamed, like I am wrong and an idiot and should have known better. I feel like a bad little boy and about five years old. This is insanity and makes life so difficult. But simply reminding myself how twisted this thinking is begins to clarify things.

I believe there might be an anxious gene that predisposes some of us to strongly react to our surroundings and to others. Somewhere along the line, we pick up food, and other things, to soothe and calm the itchy, uncomfortable emotions that result from conflict. My anxious gene has landed in my throat and has formed a sort of goiter that flares up and gets turgid and bucky at conflict. Everything gets caught there and I choke. My mom told stories of what an angsty baby I was, and only my dad had the patience to walk the floors with me as I screamed and cried the night away. I don't think the world felt right to me, and for the most part, it still doesn't. Most days I just want to scream, "What the hell is this?"

This predisposition, along with bad things that happened along the way, caused my emotional wires to tangle, but tangled wires can be untangled. Or they can simply be cut.

## My mom had the answer

I dialed the phone and waited to hear the familiar lilt of "Hellooo" that even in her final not-so-great years had a ring of hope. It's like she always thought, *This phone call could be the one to bring good news.* I mimicked "Hellooo" back to her. I was her parrot. It's why I sound like a woman to this day and always get mistaken for one on the phone. It used to mortify me, but now I roll with it. Thankfully, these days it's no longer a mortal sin to not sound like a man when you are one.

"Well, how are you, my dear?" If we have one person in this world who says something like that to us, who thinks that their life is better with us in it, shouldn't that almost be enough?

"I don't know," I said.

"What's wrong, my dear?" she asked.

"I'm having trouble."

"I know," she said. I wanted to pause a moment, but you don't do that in a southern Minnesota conversation.

I blurted out, "Everyone bugs me." I knew she knew what I meant because people bugged her, too.

**"Ach," she said. And then as if each word was to a drumbeat: "Why do you give a damn what anyone thinks of you?"**

There you go. Mom had the exact answer I needed all along. With each advancing year, it seemed she cared less and less about what other people thought of her. She struggled with it for a long time, though. She tangoed with a mix of "Screw you" and "Well, I better not stray too far from the path lest something happen." I think Dad checked out early because he suffered from it, too. Who better to say, "Come on, knock it off," than someone who has grappled with the very thing? Mom had said over and over through the years, "You're no better or no worse than anyone else," but it didn't quite sink in or at least the second half didn't.

But this landed because when Mom spoke, I always listened. Somehow, she just got me. I recall a day when I was little, and I had been racing around the house all manic and unsettled. There I was, chewing on the corners of the pillows and arms of the chair, and hiding behind the couch, all of which I did when I was anxious and sometimes still do. Something small but magical then happened. Mom caught me and said, "Here, let me teach you to write your name."

A cigarette hung out of the corner of her mouth, reminding me of the way the handle of a spoon sticks out the top of a pot on the stove. She grabbed an envelope, a piece of junk mail, flipped it over, and drew out my name. She did not write it; she sketched it slowly and with a swirl and precision that resembled the writing on a birthday cake. "There. Now you try."

I mimicked her exactly, as I did with so many things. Below where she had drawn my name, I sketched it out myself.

"Have fun with the R," she said. To this day I remember the feeling of wow, I did this. We hung it on the end of the railing of the stairs with many pieces of Scotch tape, and it stayed there until the tape gave up and it fell. It became one of the many things that always scattered our floors.

Not long after, my sister and I had a joint birthday party, and I spent hours making the invitations for the three friends I scraped together to ask. It was a six-year-old masterwork with intricate cuttings of construction paper to form a pop-up cake with candles and confetti. But it had taken so long to do one I had to abandon them, and Mom called the other moms, which I'm sure took some effort for her. When she happened upon it one day under a stack of old Sunday newspapers, she went on and on. "This is really something, what you made," she said, looking at it the way people marvel and chuckle at cards at the Hallmark store. I glowed.

Thirty years later, her new advice about dealing with others sat in my head for days: "Why do you give a damn what anyone thinks of you?" Why did I place so much importance on the thoughts and opinions of others? I think we sensitive types are prone to it.

I know I am not alone in this. I notice so many people who could use a little of my mom's advice in their own lives. I know well that constant, worried look, like a string is pulling from the inside and drawing the face into wrinkles like a drawstring purse. It's become my normal, and I see the effects in the lines and marks around my mouth and eyes. It's an overall fear that causes nervousness about the day and life in general. A constant fretful wondering of what is going to happen next and who is going to say what.

Many of the people with this look on their face are also overweight.

## Mom arranges more advice from above

My constant worry had grown into a way of being for me. It began early with random sprinklings of the nervous personality gene, then fed with lots of situations as a kid and teen that felt unsafe and random. It's nature and then, nurture.

> **The problem is, if you are a worrier, as I am, I'm not sure that it's ever going to fully go away, and worry is what makes me eat. I think it does to a lot of people. What is one to do?**

Shortly after, a big finger from somewhere flicked the side of my head as I drove to work with a bowl of oatmeal in my truck, as I did every morning. Maybe it was sent to me via one of Mom's prayers; I caught her praying a lot in her later years. Mom prayed compulsively, like I grabbed candy.

The serenity prayer for dummies downloaded out of nowhere, maybe into the oatmeal, and I ingested it. Big, stuff-of-life ideas full of large emotions always imprint on me with specific memories and images attached, like the Tupperware bowl of oatmeal on the truck seat.

> **"Focus on what you can control." A voice as plain and simple as Siri entered the side door of my brain.**

God, grant me the serenity to accept the things I cannot change, and the courage to change the things I can. Give me the wisdom to know the difference. God, grant me the guts to get spiritual when all I want to do is run, hide, and be pissy. Grant me the sense to know that it's not my job to fix the world. Help me see that what other people think of me is none of my concern; that trying to control others so that they'll treat me in a way that makes me feel okay about myself is about as twisted as it gets.

Fill my head with the sense to know that the only, the only, the only person I can change is myself. That's it. It hit me, though "God" still felt like just a word, but at least it was starting to feel like a generally good word.

A little while later, and on the same spot on the ramp to the freeway, I got a download again. I simply had to, finally, as in once-and-for-all, say fuck you (and I hate saying the F-word) to all the people in my head who get in the way of my being a rock star in my own life.

> **That might be the answer: to simply not give a damn about other people's looks, words and opinions. It sounds so basic, and a little harsh, but it's the thing that trips me up more than anything else in life.**

How could I have a spiritual awakening on the onramp to 35W scattered with thousands of cigarette butts and pop bottles of pee and the occasional woman's Payless pump and pair of underwear?

That's how it happens. Little answers to our biggest questions pop up fast and sneaky along the way in our everyday. It's often where we've never thought to look and when we least expect them. They appear almost in a flash, which might be the problem. All these happy life cues come so often and quietly that we miss them. We write them off as foolish notions. It's rather like how I will search forever for my glasses that are perched on the top of my head.

But it isn't individual people I need to shoot the F-word to. Most people, even the truly annoying ones, are just trying to do their best in the world. It's not my fellow earth soldiers I need to first give the dirty finger to and then spit the dirty word at. And the F-bomb has never rolled well off my tongue; it's like all the sugar through the years has made my tongue so sweet that it doesn't easily form.

It's not a fellow human beating heart I need to confront. It's more like a movie playing on a screen in the theater in my head. It's a pieced-together video montage assembled with some wounded video editing software. All the real and imagined things that have ever been said to me are on a loop in my brain.

> **Like an awful scrapbook, I have hung onto all the bad bits and pieces of the past, and it's now a reference book. I study what to say to be accepted and liked or not to say to avoid being rejected or scorned or humiliated.**

Another thing I do: I fret terribly over any interaction I have with someone that is anything more than "Hello." A phone call with my insurance agent. A conversation with my boss. Buying new tires from the straight grease monkey at Tires Plus. Telling my mailman that I found a letter addressed to me on the sidewalk down the street (true story). These and many more prod me to eat something. If nothing is available, even my inner cheek will do. I need to short-circuit the anxiety of the anticipation, which is really a learned response more than anything. Oh, the time and energy wasted on this.

> **It's like I have a co-dependent relationship with everyone in the world, focusing more on their feelings than my own. I even take their financial needs more into account.**

I'm hooked on the emotional payoff in the moment, as if I want the used car salesman or person behind the desk at my dentist's office to see me a certain way. I want to appear better than I think I am. I want to make them happy. If they are, I think they approve of me, and then I can approve of myself, but later I will be upset, resentful, and even a little rageful about it.

A gentle "I don't give a damn" helps so much. Because why do I care what the Tires Plus guy thinks of me? I imagine him thinking, "What a stupid fag, and he's cheap too. I'm not going to make any money off him." This is my personal history of taking other people's opinions as a judgment and the final say of who I am and of my self-worth. I give them so much say over how I feel, and then, what I do. To write it down reveals the ridiculousness of it. And the sadness.

The truth is that if he is thinking these things, well, gay and thrifty are not liabilities. They are who I am, and both are pretty fabulous ways of being. Plus, he doesn't know anything about my bank accounts, nor should he any more than I need to be responsible for him making his sales quotas.

I can choose not to give a damn. I can do this, and at the same time be courteous and reasonable. It's a matter of not giving so much of myself over to these moments because I'm sure no one else is making as big a deal of them. It gets easier and more natural every time I do it. After not too much time, it feels like a giant exhale. It's the feeling after an enormous fart.

## People pleasing feeds my food addiction

I diagnose myself as a people pleaser. I am Eric, and I am a chronic people pleaser. Oprah referred to it as the disease to please, coined from the book by Harriet Braker, I would imagine. For me, this may be my true disease, and my addictions are the side effects of the poor medicine I've been using to make myself feel better.

All the people in the know agree with the following: People pleasers avoid conflict. Rejection terrifies us. We hate disappointing people, and feel guilty when we say no. We want others to just be nice to us. We want to fit in and are easily influenced by those around us. Because our self-worth comes from the validation of others, we—and this always stings—lack self-love. Ouch. Just writing that makes me want to love myself more; it sounds like the most awful thing to starve oneself of love. I am an animal lover and a gardener, dang it. I need to treat myself at least as well as I treat my philodendron.

> **Here is how it works for me: I try to please others by being very nice and agreeable so that people will like me, and I will feel safe**

**in the world.**

If I am nice to people and they like me, at least on the surface level, they will think I am special. They won't judge, hurt, criticize, abuse, or abandon me. If I people please, there will be no conflict, and I see conflict in the world as rejection.

Childhood trauma is breeding ground for it, they say. Stuck in a small town as a shy, chubby, little gay boy, being nice was the only card I had to play to survive. If I was nice, at least no one would kill me.

When I hit my junior high years, being nice wasn't even enough. To avoid being a teenage punching bag, I went one step further and did my best to become invisible, which is passive people pleasing. At least I wasn't making waves or embarrassing anyone.

I spoke only when necessary. I attempted to dress and wear my hair and act how everyone else did, and I was so different by nature, what a losing battle that was. I hated everything that everyone else liked, so it was especially alienating.

If we hide parts of ourselves, it's impossible to ever feel truly loved or safe, so the infamous hole we're trying to fill expands as we stuff our secrets, fears, and insecurities in it. Fears and insecurities seem to validate our feelings of being less than, so we do whatever we can to quickly squelch or hide them.

**When I emotionally eat, I am stuffing down these negative feelings I feel wrong for having.**

I'm compelled to eat anytime I let my true colors show. If someone could possibly think I'm unreasonable, overly sensitive, annoying or too flamboyant, I need to feed myself. It soothes the scratchiness inside. It distracts and takes my mind off thinking I did something "wrong." When you are a people pleaser, other people's moods, foibles, and, yes, honest reactions are all fodder for a bad day. Everything stings when you are a people pleaser because acceptance by others is the ultimate goal, and anything that threatens that, threatens you.

> **Perhaps what breaks my heart the most is that a lifetime of people pleasing sort of neuters a person's sense of self.**

It keeps us from putting ourselves out there and trusting our ideas have a place in the world. We dumb ourselves down and present watered-down and faded versions of who we are. The harshest reality is that it doesn't make us any safer or more loved. It has the opposite effect as we end up not trusting ourselves, which is the only way to feel truly safe.

People pleasing destroys self-confidence and self-trust. I'll be sitting at my work computer with a work-type problem—the sort that we all have all day long—and I will get this little emotional scramble of, "I am too dumb, weak, afraid, too much of a work fraud, etc. to figure this out or to handle it." This freezes me up. I get a paper jam in my psyche, and I want to go get some food as a type of balm and avoidance. The same goes when I am hanging a picture in my house or trying to figure out why the washer isn't draining.

So, what do we people pleasing, compulsive, emotional eaters do?

## When enough is enough

Breaking points can suck, but they usually mark the beginning of the end, so we're actually lucky when they happen. I had a gradual five-year one where more and more I said to myself, "That's it. It's time to change the channel or put in another movie." The dam finally broke for me (Mom helped take a jackhammer to it).

> **I couldn't give up one more precious breath or waste another brain cell worrying about what others thought, said, or did.**

Once you get it in your head that it's time to stop being a people pleaser, you get a little jolt in your system anytime you catch yourself doing it, which is helpful. These moments that popped up challenged me to forget all the things said and done in the past that stuck in me like a sliver and infected my whole being. It's a mental act of erasing them on the chalkboard of my mind when they appear, which is a very helpful image; it's like these old thoughts turn into chalk dust and blow away. I use this with any thoughts that are simply not helpful or in my best interest, like when I think someone is right and I am wrong.

It circles back to not giving a damn about what other people think, which is easily misinterpreted as being a rude prick, but there's plenty of room for compassion and caring without being a people pleaser. I can be available to people when necessary while still letting go of the voices in my head. The answer is to simply not give a damn about all that. To let it go. Finally. It's garbage of the brain.

How do I personally do this? First off, I face that at the core, I'm so afraid of people. This might be what sends me to eat the most—my constant fear of just about anybody and any interaction. Nothing soothes and distracts from this like eating. I'm terrified of humiliation, of being wrong, and of not being enough. I view the world as a WWI battleground, like my grandpa fought on with rats the size of Chihuahuas. Maybe that's why I loved wearing his old winter coat when I was my heaviest. It fit me, so I must have been his size and his protective spirit was in that old coat.

I'm out in an open field and crouching in trenches, and I'm running and hiding behind scorched trees and then deciphering the motives of my enemy, who I know is out there. I can sense them on the gray, murky horizon. It's a general threatening presence, humming like overhead power lines, and I build a little defense in my head and think, they are plotting against me, and how can I gird myself against them? How can I present myself so they don't attack me? Do I Benedict Arnold it and go to the side of the enemy and betray myself? Yes, I do. That's exactly what I do. The upside? I've developed a certain psychic intuition from it all.

Next, I force myself to just turn the terrible TV movie of the week off.

Yes, some people might be out to get me. Those types exist. The soldier who appears out of nowhere over the ridge in slow motion like in a war movie is a reality in life, especially at the office. But in quiet, thoughtful moments, what comes to me is that no one cares as much as I think. People are far more concerned with themselves than with me. People are not against me, they are for themselves. Most of us are at about the same level of wounded and scared and insecure, I believe.

The drive home from work is a tough time to remember all this. It's a big mental family dinner in my truck where everyone is arguing and yelling. The 20-minute drive is a reworking of every prickly conflict from the day and my mind swirls and relives it. Sometimes I catch a driver next to me on the highway looking at me, maybe in wonder over who I am talking to so rapid fire. It's all the people I've encountered over the past eight hours, and I work through the awkward angst of my reactions toward them. The justifications and the "Well, that's all her" or the "I'm just going to shut my mouth from now on."

**When I get home, all I want to do is eat and eat as the dust settles from a day of people pleasing.**

The anxiousness around things I did wrong begins to crawl up my legs and take little bites like bedbugs; eventually they get to my head, and things start flying around. It's the scene in *The Wizard of Oz* when Dorothy is in her bedroom and the twister has sucked her and Toto up into it. We see cows and an old lady in a rocking chair, and then Elvira Gulch pedaling her bike, and then she explodes into the witch.

This is when I find myself walking back and forth to the kitchen for crackers, Pop Chips, supper leftovers, or whatever will distract me. Distraction is what it's all about, along with quieting the voices.

And there it is. There's the moment when I can let go of the kite.

**I can simply not care and let it go and it will be fine. I can stop trying to make sense of something that is just as easily forgotten. I remind myself: What they all think of me is none of my business.**

If I sensed negative emotions in someone, I remind myself we are not responsible for other people's emotions. That's the bottom line. It's as solid a fact as gravity, but it takes a while to sink in and settle into the psyche.

Do I see the rest of the world as a target, an arcade of people I am trying to knock off center? I do not. Do I judge others throughout the day for their words and actions? Of course I do. We all do. Let's just own it. But do I want to destroy them? I do not. Usually, I can even see their side of the story.

But I will waste hours over what I did or said or the look they gave me. I'm harder on myself than I am on strangers and bitchy co-workers.

So, the only thing left to do is to not give a fuck about leftover voices in my head.

> **But again, if a person is like me and doesn't like to swear, what does one use for their mantra? What's the personally palatable version of I don't give a fuck?**

I don't give a damn doesn't have the same oomph. FU seems to work.

Then I realize I don't even need to say FU. "No, thank you" works great. It makes it not such a big deal.

No, thank you. I don't need to care what you think of me. No thank you, I'll be just fine without your approval. When I say this to myself, and even tactfully out loud on occasion, I feel peace. Self-love and self-respect begin to fill me. It's warm, like a shot of emotional tequila.

## Quite simply, we are not responsible for other people's emotions

We've all heard it a thousand times, but every time I do, I also hear a voice say, "Well, yeah, in theory, that's nice. In the perfect family or workplace, but that can't work for me." But it's one of the great truths of living, I think, and one of the hardest to embrace. When I view it from a sort of clinical perspective, it's crystal clear. We don't have the responsibility, or even the ability, to make other people happy or sad or anything in between. I mean, who do we think we are?

Then I say to myself, "Well, sure, I can." I can tell them, "Yes, I will go to the movie with you," when I don't want to, and this makes them happy. Or I can say no to weekend plans when I don't want to, and won't they be sad? Disappointing people still bothers me. The rational side of the coin: Maybe they will be a little giddy or let down at first, but it'll fade and they will get over it. Plus, do I really think they are so fragile they can be broken by my decision? Isn't it better we both live our lives as we'd like and have a relationship based in truth? We both get to be mindful of what we want and the two do not need to get tangled up with each other.

At first, not monitoring other people's emotions feels like dropping off a senior dog at the animal shelter. It seems cruel and also scary because I've been so used to basing my own emotions off others. But the honesty and lightness of not doing it settles in the more I sit with it.

Again, I remind myself: I am not responsible for other people's emotions. Even when I think I am, I'm not having any real effect on their happiness. They may tell me I am or plaster on a smile to make me think it, but I'm not. Plus, there is a huge difference between momentarily disappointing someone and purposefully hurting them. The two can register as the same to me.

At first, it seems unthinkable to be anything less than nice and agreeable, but with practice, it soon feels quite normal and natural. It feels healthy and rather badass and the way life is meant to feel. It takes practice, and there may be failure, but also, I don't think it has to take a long time to get there. You can decide to do it in the morning and by the afternoon, be considerably more truthful and kind, which is sort of the opposite of being just nice.

I have a couple of folks who I let manipulate me a little. These are people I know will never get it, and to hold stiff boundaries creates more fuss than it's worth. It disturbs too much of the peace. I am a boundary realist with them, and yes, I do have some boundaries with them, but the bar is higher for what I will put up with. You can only have a couple of these in life, and as long as you know the truth of the situation, it's fine.

# These are just thoughts we have... and nothing more

The annoyance I feel towards others, along with my fear of them, is often epic, but maybe the thing is, these are just meaningless thoughts. They're like ash in a fire pit that looks solid, but then you poke them with a stick and poof, they vanish. They break into a million little shards and float away.

**Thoughts don't deserve the respect we often give them. They are fleeting little pot-stirrers that can be ignored and they disappear.**

As a little boy, all I had was my thoughts. I always felt so alone with my unrelenting feelings of being not right in the world. I grew up alone with no one to talk to about them. I had no solid best friend or anyone I felt comfortable asking, "Do you feel this way, too?" These days, I could Google it. Seriously, the internet might be a comfort to the outcast kids in this way, though I'm sure social media would have been a devastation to me. I pray, literally, for outcast kids and new members of the fat kid's club. I hope they can find community online if they aren't able to where they live.

Growing up as a closeted gay kid, I hid a big chunk of my real self. I got into the practice of repressing emotions of any true kind, assuming they were my own little misguided beliefs and feelings. When it's out in the open and accepted, sexuality doesn't seem like that big a deal. When you have to hide it, it's everything. Shame becomes the way you view the world and it seems nothing in your life can rise above the greatest shame you feel.

All I knew was to try to think my way through all the confusing and cruel things in the world. My whole everything was in my head because that's how I had made it through. I tried to make sense of it all and strategize how to survive. Dad didn't talk. Dad looked at me a certain way. I thought a lot about it. Mom sulked because Dad sulked. I tried to think it through and figure it out. Then suddenly, all the kids at school hated me. Why, 12-year-old Eric, could this suddenly come out of nowhere? My thoughts that were trying to figure things out fed my compulsive eating and created a down parka coat that covered and smothered and weighed me down.

Random, unpleasant thoughts seem to rule the world. I witness, especially in the workplace, a need for drama thoughts; these are the heightened, active version of the ongoing compulsive thoughts that fill our days. I see people create drama all the time, around the most everyday circumstances. It's an addiction to drama, really, and these drama thoughts create so much unnecessary stress and heartache. Once you notice it at work, you can't stop noticing it because it's an office epidemic. "I can't believe she didn't add paper to the copier." "I think he's been gone this week because something major happened in the meeting on Monday." "Did you see Mary go into the big boss's office?"

Then I thought about how I do this in my personal life as well. It may spring from the belief that as-is, I am not enough, and I need to create "more." This is also when it happens at work, I believe. When our jobs basically bore us, we need to create some excitement. We write a soap opera to star in to make the day more interesting. If we have work insecurities, which we all do, we try to make ourselves feel like more by making others seem like less.

My thoughts are the junior high boys in my head. My thoughts percolate into fear of humiliation and uncertainty, and lack of control. They tell me I'll be beaten up and abandoned on the side of the road. My thoughts make me feel like I've disappointed or abandoned someone else, which is the worst of all to me. It ties a flu-like knot in my stomach and locks my jaw.

**These thoughts and emotions still have me stuck in my adolescent mind of being terrified of others; I want them to go away, but think I need them to survive. I act in whatever way I think might make them like or at least tolerate me.**

That is at the core of why I am so compelled, Pavlov's dog style, to eat and to stuff and to smother myself. Going for food makes the thoughts go away for a little while because they get so heavy and thick and ominous in the head. Eating is a way to avoid them and tamp them down to be dealt with later when they have really festered.

We all have them, these thoughts like rodents, but as I sit and observe them,

I see they are like leaves flying around random and with no real weight or effect on anything. I see that they are nothing and as solid as a dandelion head.

> **Instead of these random thoughts, I can ask myself, "What do I want to think about?"**

It's like the giant exhale that happens when you realize you're holding your breath and sucking in your gut, and then you let it go.

## Feel the feelings

Another phrase we've all heard: Feel the feelings. It sounds as pleasant as a bad cold, but it helps so much when I do it, which isn't always. I bucked it for a long, long time—like 40 years.

First, I had it in my head that my feelings were silliness I made up because of my various faults, ineptitudes, and slanted views on life. I basically scolded myself for having emotions; I thought they were the lame side effect of my overly sensitive nature. Plus, if I sat with the emotion, it would be intolerable, so I needed to switch to the mode of quickly fixing and then moving on from the emotion. In addition to being painful, I thought sitting with the emotion made it worse. It would poison me, which is ironic because not feeling the feeling is what poisons us. Another irony was some of the new-age thinking I immersed myself in seemed to teach us to only focus on the positive in life, which I interpreted as blocking the negative feelings.

> **As repugnant as the notion sounds, I began to make a conscious choice to feel my feelings, good and bad. Full disclosure: this was when I was close to 50.**

The more I did it, the more it became clear that it's the only way to go. Fifteen minutes of owning how I feel and sitting in the smell of it somehow disempowers the emotion. It might be at the core of the phrase, what we resist, persists.

Feeling the feeling has magical powers. Here's how it goes for me:

A bad feeling builds in my throat and then my stomach after I believe I've disappointed someone or made a fool of myself. If I'm not able to figure out how to do something at work or in the garage, or I get an email that I spaced something, these will do it too. I then think I am selfish or a fraud or a screw-up or a loser, which, when I step away from it, is such a child-like way to view it.

But if I feel the feeling, it sort of diffuses the bomb. Sitting with it, versus running to get some food to quell the nausea, allows it to run its course and to reveal itself for what it is: simply something that happened that doesn't declare who I am and doesn't need to be a big deal. Feelings are legitimate and valid and no big deal, all at the same time

It's rather like everything in the world is neutral, and it's the meaning that we attach to things that make them awful to us. Feelings not felt are huge, unknown, and terrifying. When they are felt, they are minor. Very little in life is a big deal, I dare say.

> **Our feelings carry pretty valuable information if viewed without judgment. Emotions don't appear out of thin air; they are hinged to something that has happened to us.**

We don't have to let them control us, but we also can listen to them for clues. They can be a type of intuition and also, a best friend eavesdropper who knows the whole story and shows us that there is more than meets the eye. Feelings show us what we might be overlooking. One time I had doom-and-gloom vibes about an upcoming directing gig, but I dismissed my feelings and soldiered on, and it turned out to be just an awful experience. It's like we need to listen with one ear to our feelings. Generalized insecurity and fear can live in them, but also valuable life cues.

Another magical thing that happens when I sit with my emotions is I don't feel so isolated from the rest of the world. I somehow join a community of people like me who are just doing our best to navigate this crazy world. I feel a rightful part of everything. I see everyone as individuals—not a united force of bad—and no different than me, and then whoa, I actually like people!

> **I simply cannot be the only one with all these insecurities and bad thoughts. We are all a little bruised by the world and are just doing our best.**

This helps me see a thought for what it is and simply let it pass through me without blowing it up like a balloon and waiting for the pop.

# Chapter 15

## Remembering to turn onto the sunny side of the street

O ne day I had a moment like a flash bulb went off. It occurred to me that when I mostly stayed away from sugar, cookies, candy, cakes, etc., and if I needed to binge a little, I did it on fruit and giant bowls of vegetables, I had more days like the following:

I was now just under 200 pounds, but I had 20 or so extra pounds of loose flab, like Ziplock bags of melted ice hanging on my lower back, inner thighs, and lower belly. I was about to slide into the same old thinking pattern of, this is so gross. Then I thought, it's fine. I have clothes that fit, and I look pretty good in them. If I don't use all my brain bandwidth on old spinnings, I can think about other things that light me up like making my house nicer or planning a trip or working on a painting or plotting my next garden project. Or I could just stay in an overall lighter state of being.

Flash-bulb moments can only happen when one's inner vision isn't all fuzzy from hangovers of both the food and alcohol variety. (Food hangovers are real and about the same as booze ones, but with less of a headache.) I would even have what I saw as the most golden of thoughts: Yes, I've got some weight to lose, and it's fine. I can lose it over the next few months; it's no big deal.

**To accept where I am at—and be hopeful at the same time—continues to be my ultimate.**

It's easier on a beautiful Sunday morning when I have no work, no personal commitments, and just a lovely day before me. When the world starts to cast a shadow that crosses over me, and people start knocking at my door, bugging me, poking and needling me, and attacking me (if only in my head), what then?

## How do we feel safe in the world?

How do you live without the general anesthesia of sugar and the preoccupying balm of a lot of food? I think the secret is to craft a life that you don't need to run from.

**It keeps coming back to this compact phrase: We can do whatever we want in this world as long as we're kind, respectful, and responsible. Add a healthy dose of not giving a damn about what others think, and remembering nothing in life is as big of a deal as we often imagine. The more I tell myself these things, the more the old and tired voices in my head seem to wear themselves out.**

When I remember these things, the volume goes down on thoughts that everyone out there has the goal of knocking me off balance and pushing me out of the circle of living. And I feel less like I have to be nice to people to survive. The world's war cry of "Who does he think he is" mutes. Silly, stupid, sissy, fatso, fag wears out like the 45s of Elton John and Dolly Parton I played on my little record player until the needle just slid across the disc.

The phrases "People aren't against you, they are for themselves" and "What people think of me is none of my business" sparkle when I think of them. They're written on slips of paper in my wallet and above my computer monitor.

For so much of my life, I was too afraid to do or say something that would jeopardize someone being on my side. Rather than standing up to people, I would retreat. To stand up for myself was to make myself vulnerable, like a sunflower in the wind, and I could get snapped off at the stem, and then what? What do I do when no one is in my corner? I would die like a houseplant that gets stuck away in another room, and no one ever waters it. The reality is that people who are on our side only because we are nice to them really aren't on our side. They might be, but they could also turn on us in a heartbeat.

I wish that's what I had picked up in school instead of a constant fear of others, an insane need to be liked by everyone, and a never-ending need to eat.

To do what you need to do to make yourself truly happy can feel like an enormous decision and too gigantic of a move. I'm talking about the pure, down at the center, this is just between you and your higher power kind of happiness, which might actually be more about being content than happy. However we phrase it, we all know what we're talking about, and it can seem impossible.

Many of us die long before we actually kick the bucket, I think. Addiction is a way of dying before you actually die, because in a way, you are trying to kill the bad feelings inside, or at least, make them tolerable. Ironically, the bad feelings survive, and all the good stuff in us perishes.

> **How can we not die decades before we really die? This is what it comes down to in my worldview: To do (or maybe more important, not do) whatever it is you need to do so you aren't compelled to soothe and comfort and distract with food or drink or gambling or shopping or whatever the addiction of choice is.**

To not die early, quite simply, needs to be the #1 goal. This becomes more and more obvious as we grow older. From my experience, it becomes paramount in one's 40s. Hopefully, you'll get it before then, but if you haven't, the 40s and 50s will help make the change. The achy joints from excess weight talk loudly. And the sick and tiredness of overeating, and other addictions, will likely overcome you. You'll crash and burn or one day you'll just go, "Oh, there is another way to do this."

To make such a bold move as to go towards happiness, well, this can seem too renegade for daily life. It feels so rebellious in our society, and how ridiculous is that? Recently at work, I sat at my desk and observed a catty exchange between co-workers in a series of emails I was CC-ed on. They were verbally sniping at each other, and I wrote on a sheet of paper, "Could anyone really blame me for not wanting to be a part of all this? Workplaces are dens of vipers."

> **Bold moves toward happiness are different for everyone. Many have situations that would seem impossible to change. I so understand that. I can only tell you a few of the somewhat daring shifts I've made.**

I left a high-paying corporate job for the non-profit world. I've often reduced my work hours to 75% to take art classes on Friday; this sometimes took playing hardball with a boss and risking them just saying "ba-bye." I've also left a job because that "one person" we all have at work became more than I could handle; I lived on savings for a few months until I landed the next gig. I went back to school to get a graphic design degree at 40. I left the theater, a life I had always known, because it finally clicked that it was too much for me. I've paid the money to join a gym to get fit (it doesn't sound bold, but it was for me at the time). I saved the money and bought a little parcel in the country to retreat to. I've dropped people in my life because they weren't good for me to be around—there's no gentle to way to say that one.

These are a few I've done that have inched me closer to happiness and helped me create a life where I don't need the soothing effects of food, and also drink, as much. I still do at times, but every day I'm moving in the direction of not.

# V

# Part Five

*Staying below 200 pounds*

# Chapter 16

## The friendly binge

I'm not sure any of us who turn to food for comfort, love, and security ever completely get over it. We food addicts are powerless under its spell, no matter what stage of the process we're at. We don't want to eat, but it's as if we can't help ourselves. Something inside just makes us do it.

Life as a grown-up is not much different than when I would come home from school after a bad day and eat everything in sight. Giving up compulsive eating when stressed or scared or lonely or hurt seems unthinkable. Quite simply, getting completely over my food compulsion may not be in the cards, plus the perfectionism around all the typical black-or-white diet maxims kept sabotaging me. Not eating carbs, for example, was like holding a beach ball under the water. When I couldn't contain it any longer, it shot up, hit me in the face, and left a black eye.

I have many, many good days when I don't need to eat to soothe. But I have not-so-good days, too. How could I ever make it without my old friend food waiting on deck when needed?

I needed to find a way to make my food addiction work in my life so I could lose weight, because I want to be thin more than anything in life. Nothing else makes sense or matters if I am overweight. I decided to keep my old friend close by, but I've cleaned up his act.

**I've never lost the urge to binge—I may never—so I friendly binge, as I call it.**

When I need to eat, eat, eat, I give in, but in as healthy a way as possible. I do half a watermelon rather than half a cake. A bag (or two) of microwave popcorn rather than a bag of corn chips. Wasa crackers, which are thin and very low-calorie, are also a go-to.

If I need more indulgence, more associative comfort, several bowls of Fiber One cereal remind me of being a kid and eating Bran Flakes at our kitchen table. My mom, believe it or not, didn't let Fruit Loops or Count Chocula or other fun, sugary cereals into the house. She probably didn't want them tempting her. Perhaps that little gift is why I can get satisfied and calmed down by bingeing on healthier foods. The plus side of being an addict is I can also get easily hooked on healthier things. Fiber One is handy because it comes boxed with two separate bags inside, so I keep my binge to one bag in a day, and no real weight-gain damage is done.

A bowl of fruit the size of a hat filled with strawberries, grapes, canned peaches and pineapple, chopped apples, and sliced bananas can be like cake to me. When it's topped with Greek yogurt and some Fiber One, it's as glorious as a birthday cake.

I've been known to eat five apples and three bananas in a day. Going for a banana is my version of grabbing a Snickers in the checkout line at Target. Apples work so well because they're sweet, and the crunch works out my anxiety. Texture is such an essential part of my healthy binge foods. The action of eating them is like a stress-reducing massage.

**My healthy binge approach is harm reduction, not perfection. But perfection has never worked for me with food.**

Perfectionism is a time-tested recipe for failure. Some might say I'm ignoring the heart of the matter, and there is still something deeper causing me to go to food. To this I would say, yes, there are deeper things sending me to food, but this works for me and has worked for me while I continue to work on the underlying issues, which I believe is a life-long journey. Quite simply, it got me to 180 pounds. I think this could work for many who need to lose the weight. The friendly-binge is one of the biggest tools in my toolbox to get thin and stay thin.

## Though food sometimes needs to be challenged

Often when I have the emotional urge to eat, I give in without thinking because I'm resigned to the fact that food will always triumph. Food is a Las Vegas casino, and "the house always wins." But sometimes, I will wait it out. I sit still, breathe slowly and deeply, and really feel whatever discomfort I am experiencing. I remind myself that it doesn't matter what someone else thinks of me. All will be well. I can figure out whatever is making me feel like an imposter. I have helpers "up there and out there." Then wow—calm, reason, and a lightness of spirit wash over me.

Drinking a lot of water also helps settle me down. Dehydration makes me sad and confused, and I can literally feel myself brighten and lift when I force water, like a wilted plant slowly lifts its leaves when given a drink. Slight hunger + water + breathing + positive thoughts = a warm, calming buzz, like the best cup of coffee in the world. It feels like a connection to something higher within myself.

## A sane eating day

I friendly binge a couple times a week. 95% of the time I eat pretty clean, and I will say, a few hunger pangs are necessary when a person is losing and maintaining weight. I try to love them when they rumble in me and remember how they make me feel clean and empty and light, because they can also feel lonely and can make me nervous.

**From my experience, calories count the most for weight loss and management.**

Low carb, Mediterranean eating, plenty of fruits and vegetables, protein at every meal—these all bring better health. But at its most basic, 100 calories of carrots and 100 calories of Hershey's kisses have the same effect on weight, I am convinced. But the carrots are better for you and fill you up more.

People often want to know what I eat in a day, especially if it's someone who wants to lose weight. They'll ask if it was my switch to a mostly vegetarian diet or my drastically limiting sugar or my constantly eluding Funyuns. In the end, it's mostly a general sense of how many calories my 170-ish pound body that does some sort of exercise most days needs to maintain itself. Tracking my calories and food intake on various apps has helped with this, but it's more internal than that. Having been on a diet (at least in my head) most days since I was 10, I have a pretty good sense of the number of calories in foods. Also, I simply accept that fruit, vegetables, beans, whole grain crackers, fish, eggs, and veggie burgers, to name a few choices, are the best way to go.

A sample day: 45-calorie toast with powdered peanut butter and sugar-free jam. An egg, black beans, vegetables, and a little cheese scrambled together and folded in a tortilla. I'll repeat the egg scramble later in the morning if needed. An apple and powdered peanut butter. A can of tuna with mayo or a veggie burger and a big salad with beans, onions, and vegetables and light Ranch dressing, plus a couple Wasa crackers. Greek yogurt, fruit of some sort, and my homemade granola (oatmeal, cinnamon, and Truvia brown sugar sprayed with cooking spray, microwaved for a minute, and cooled in the freezer). A couple more Wasa crackers with sugar-free jam. Another apple, banana, bowl of watermelon, or cup of berries or canned peaches. Perhaps a peanut butter and jelly sandwich in the later afternoon (powdered peanut butter and sugar-free jelly). A large bowl of vegetables with a half of a cup of rice or beans or lentils and a faux-meat version of chicken, meatballs, or some type of fish. An iced decaf coffee with soy milk and sugar-free flavored syrup and maybe a Wasa cracker with jam and cream cheese.

When I eat a lot vegetables, I'm amazed at how much food I can have and stay below 2,400 or so calories, which is about the amount I need to maintain my weight. At the same time, it's amazing how quickly I can use up these calories. In the end, I think we all need to get a general sense of how many calories our bodies need to first lose and then maintain our weight. A calorie counting app is great for this. Then we pick and choose the foods we love the most and fit them into the plan.

> **It may require falling in love with some new foods, like zucchini for example. I love it and three cups has fewer than 100 calories. When you add Parmesan cheese and garlic it's like a bowl of pasta.**

As I've said, the math problem part of losing weight is the easy part. Getting ourselves to not blow it all with emotional eating is the equation to keep working on. And that's a daily and probably lifelong activity.

## Artificial sweeteners

My typical eating day (though there is never anything typical about my eating) brings up the inevitable topic of artificial sweeteners. I work at eliminating sugar as best as I can. I have joint issues, and I've read that sugar is basically broken glass on our joints. Holidays are a sugary slippery slope, but I bake with Truvia. I could be a Truvia spokesperson.

There is a lot of information out there on artificial sweeteners. My ultimate way to go would be to use none of them, as well as no sugar, but that's never going to be an option for me, at least that's how it feels now. Truvia seems to be the most natural choice. But I still eat and drink things that contain the others, as well.

Am I an artificial sweetener evangelist? No. Did it play a part in my weight loss? Most certainly. I have a sweet tooth. I ate more pink and blue packets than I care to think about; all the fake crystals may still live in my cells. It's quite possible we don't have a clue yet about the long-term effects of artificial sweeteners. But I do believe that if the use of artificial sweeteners will help you to lose weight, like they did for me, they're healthier than being 100 pounds over weight.

In the end, artificial sweeteners are a highly personal choice. I wish I could quit them, to quote *Brokeback Mountain*, but I am not yet there. I do believe giving myself a slow drip of sweetness throughout my day generally keeps my sweet tooth alive. But I also think I crave that sweetness on an emotional level and artificial sweetener helps with that without the calories. For now, the use of artificial sweeteners is a chapter in my life that does not yet have a conclusion.

# Chapter 17

## The candy bar binge

Whenever I get arrogant enough to think that I have this whole emotional eating/food obsession thing licked, I put five to ten pounds back on. It's all like a game of Sorry to me. A few moves forward, then one back. A jump way ahead, and then I get sent back home.

> **It usually happens over Christmas when everything I'm powerless to is everywhere. Also, when I'm insecure at work.**

There was a period when people were getting fired like crazy. My boss was aloof, and my co-workers all seemed to be against me, though I get the sense everyone who works has the same concerns. We all think we have these very specific issues, but if you'd run a scrolling marquee at the office like stock prices run around the room on a trading floor, there would be the same five or so: 1. My boss doesn't even know what I do. 2. My co-workers don't respect me. 3. All we do is spin our wheels. 4. Nothing I do makes a difference to anyone. 5. I feel like an impostor, and I'm going to be found out.

So, there are days, weeks even, when I go back to food in a big way, though each time I do it's a little less so.

Bad feelings about work or the holidays start the ball rolling again. The crack always forms in the late afternoon; it's a dark, fuzzy-headed, cloudy, and confusing time for me. If nothing is handy it may not happen, but if there is, then here we go.

It could start right after Halloween when everyone is trying to get rid of their Halloween candy or at Christmas. All the Christmas crack, peanut butter blossoms with the chocolate star pressed in the middle, gingerbread men with crooked icing smiles, and chocolate oranges that break open when you smack them begin the quick descent. It's always with a mask of denial like this time will be different than the 50 million previous.

So, the remedy to all this would be to not pick up that one candy bar, but it's so lovely. How could anyone resist? It's not only how the sugar hits and alters me, and the caramel soothes and calms; the little candy bars are like ornaments that hang on the Christmas tree. I love them so much. I seek them out. They mesmerize and hypnotize me.

**And how does one resist the call of a piece of cake? Nothing else matters when in its clutches.**

Nothing troubles you when under its spell. Cakes signify celebrations like weddings, graduations, and retirement parties. After it's cut, those of us who feel somehow left out of everything, whether by our own devices or others, sit with our big piece and even a second and third and commune with it and wonder, why not me? I'm special, too. The cake tells us we are. At the moment, it's all about the cake or the candy bars.

There are even 10 to 15 minutes of rational self-talk. "You can have a fun-size Snickers, Eric." You can be like everyone and indulge in that little log of goodness. Everyone does it with a glimmer of a thought that they shouldn't, that it's a tiny bit naughty, but most have one or two and then move on with their day.

I stare at it and rhapsodize how divine it is and how it's such a heavenly little treat. The imprint on the bottom of the candy bar is so beautiful and perfect with the little indentations from perhaps a delicately embossed waxy paper that the newly formed bar lands on to cool. They no doubt get pooped out of a big candy robot, and when they do, a little chocolate pompadour swirls on the top. They're little jewels and so perfect, especially when they are fresh and haven't sat around a while in an orange, plastic Jack-O-Lantern.

I could enjoy it slow and proud like Grandma gave it to me for being a good boy. I could eat it as if with white gloves and it's on a frilly, floral-painted China plate, and as neatly and slowly as if with a knife and fork. Then I'd pat my mouth with a napkin and allow the joy that comes from small rewards of a favorite treat settle in. A sort of relaxed bliss washes through my body. I smile small and move on with my day. One snack-size candy bar at 75 calories, and it's fine.

That's how it goes about one in a hundred times.

If it's fresh, I will enjoy the first two or three. If the flavors that come forth when the little bit of natural chocolate, butter, and anonymous goodness are still there, it's a hit of dopamine. If it's old, the chemicals in the candy bar are what remain. The flavor is flat, and the smell is strange, like a chemical toilet. But I'll eat it at this stage, too, because all I want now is to not feel something that's bothering me.

The sugary caramel and chocolate gently resist my bite and the hard waxy shell holds on as long as it can until my teeth press down enough to break through.

> **The chocolate resists in the same way I do until I realize it's hopeless, and I sort of jump into the smooth, creamy pool of comfort and familiarity, and I know that nothing else matters.**

Nothing can hurt or annoy or offend or worry or distress while that is in my mouth.

Then I swallow, and everything that became quiet in that moment of enjoyment explodes, and it's pissed at me for even thinking I could have just one or two. Rather than moving on to the next thing in my day, something gets off track.

> **In a desperate attempt to quiet the sugars, because it is the sugar talking, I'll self-talk that it's all good and not a problem. A little**

**candy bar never did a soul any harm, but the sugar is in me, and it needs to be fed.**

It needs companions, and the flood of guilt and shame and remorse and, yeah, self-loathing and disgust are bubbling up and over. I slap myself inside for being so clueless and in denial that I thought I could have one, and then I'm sad that I spoiled my day of no sugar. I have turned into a werewolf.

The only thing that soothes is more of the same, and then candy bars get collected from any source I can find. They get stuffed in the pockets of my cargo pants and carried back to my desk, where I will arrange them in a seemingly innocent little pile. I arrange a little kid's party near my keyboard and mouse. I eat, and no concentration or focus on anything can happen anymore because the beast must be fed, and the sugar is in me. The jagged edges of the little crystals scratch my insides, and my blood thickens, and my mental state is now somewhere between a dark abstract painting and a carnival.

I go back for more, probably 20 times. I sometimes carry a sheet of paper, so it looks like I am doing work, like running a little errand in the office. I think everyone is watching because I am so aware of what I am doing. Around 3:30, a wave of stomach nausea and cramps begin, so I stop. After an hour, I start in again because I've ruined this day, and so much damage has been done. I am at 5,000 calories of gook for sure. Only more candy will make it feel better. I am basically stuffing it in me like packing in the last pair of flip-flops in an overstuffed suitcase for vacation. My stomach is so full that the food is piling up past my esophagus, like when our toilet on the farm wouldn't flush for a few days.

**I feel like a giant, overstuffed bag of garbage, and this is how broken my thinking is around all of this.**

I comfort how puffy and out-of-control I feel by nibbling on more. Now I am nursing on them. It's like I'm rubbing them on my wrist to make me feel okay like earthy-crunchy types do with calming essential oils. M&Ms don't take up much space, so they can't make me fat; that's another mind worm of mine. Candy basically melts into a little serum that drips like an IV into me, and if it doesn't take up any stomach real estate, then no harm is done.

I go for some more, and I can't even taste it at this point. My tongue is a slab, my taste buds are dead, and even though a little sweetness does still register, I am now a candy zombie. When you eat a lot of candy at once, it soon tastes all the sugary same, sort of like a public bathroom smells.

This is insanity. I can't do this anymore, I think. My head is quite literally in my hands like the painting of the condemned sinner.

A body itch begins, like many mosquito bites, when I've eaten a bunch of crap. Self-groping follows. It's like the sugar and all the other fake ick that sweetens and makes cheap treats palatable starts to burn and itch and scrape inside. Sugar is like broken glass to our joints and our cells.

This shifts my brain to an even more irrational place, and I feel my body all over to see if I've gained any weight, to see if any little fat cells have popped up, like a layer of bubble wrap. My head is twisted sideways. I swear I can detect noticeable weight gain from a couple of hours of this eating.

I feel around my middle, where the first few pounds appear. My pants aren't yet snug, just a little rubbing, so I eat another Snickers. Now I'm desperate and clinging to the hope that I haven't screwed up my weight loss journey, but what's the point in stopping now? The damage is done, and these bad characters don't let go easily.

Not everyone has endless amounts of snacks at work like I did at several of my jobs through the years. But even if it's not part of a person's workplace, they're always easy to get. A junkie will always find a way.

I remember the food drawer of one of my bosses at the phone company. It was infamous, and she would have a row of saltines and a jar of grape jelly that was the perfect sweet and salty mix, and she would work her way through it like a deck of cards in the late afternoon. Women had it tough in the workplace in the 90s.

After an afternoon like this, the glacier of eating crap has begun to move. The volcano of bad eating hasn't erupted, but it's puffing smoke. It's heating up inside me, all the sugar taking hold and forming its crystal-like structures.

Soon it will blow, and the lava will invade the village like caramel goo.

Eating like this is an odd mix of caring only about comfort in the present moment, while also steeped in the regrets of the past, and worries of the future. I'm trying to ease my fear of the world that runs through my veins. I don't care about the effect on my body. For the moment, the relief is more important than staying thin. What it's doing to my body inside, under the fat, certainly doesn't register.

The only thing to do at this point is to muscle through the stink of the situation.

I write a note on a Post-it to myself that reads: Don't do it. It will make you feel awful. I try to remind myself: You can do whatever you want in life, but not this.

> **A therapist once told me that overeating affects our brain and body chemistry as much as drugs and alcohol.**

I imagine how it goes down to the gut, that mysterious place past the back of the throat I would stare at endlessly as a kid. I'd look into the bathroom mirror as I tried to get an idea of what was going on down in my body that was so strange and fat and foreign to me.

I picture the assault on my organs, my everything down in there. My stomach takes on the avalanche and stretches out to accommodate the amount of food that would fill a plastic grocery sack. Then my body begins to feel like my truck when I try to start it in the dead of winter with the lights on and the radio and fan at full blast. The body slows way down, trying to send all the energy to digest this onslaught, and then all the poor little organs kick into overdrive to manage the sugar and fat and salt. All the weird chemicals that exist in little candy bars, oatmeal pies, Cool Whip, and Snack Pack pudding pollute and make everything off-kilter.

Because I came back from obesity, and the creep of weight gain is always in my head, maybe I'll stay thin as I get older because when all I want to do is eat candy bars, I wonder. Maybe the constant awareness I have of my weight will keep me from becoming like the boys from high school I see on Facebook that are getting big. I wonder if they see what's happening to them, but mostly, I bask in the karma.

Side note: I think it was because of my sissiness they were tough on me. The fat was just icing on the cake. Straight fat guys are like having a sitcom playing all the time. They raise the jolly quotient of a room. They are everyday Santas. Gay fat guys are archery targets, especially in high school. We are giant hassocks with bullseyes.

What if I got big again and became a huge, old, fat guy? It could seem like the ultimate, "Oh, yeah, well, screw you" to the world. I'd flip the middle finger to society, which, as hard as I try, I still hold a grudge against. If I got fat again and let myself become Jabba the Hut, I would laugh in the face of the world I've always tried to fit into.

I would also have a response to the people who verbally toss out things like, "Wow, he's getting so thin, is there something wrong with him? Does he have manorexia?" Or when I turn down a cookie, and they go, "Oh, please, you're skin and bones, what have you got to worry about, one cookie isn't going to hurt you. I didn't think you had all those issues anymore." Casual comments like this make me want to "fly on top of their heads," as my mom would say about people who annoyed her.

It irks me so much when someone says, "Oh, you are so good." I know I'm not all that cleaned up inside, and again, it makes me feel different, and all I want is to fit in. Plus, it draws attention to my body, like it did when I was a little fat boy, and makes me want to generally scream, "Mind your own damned business and worry about yourself!"

If I got fat, I would say, "Well, screw you all. Do you think I can handle a cookie? Well, look at me now, I'm a big, fat tub of lard." I'd be in familiar territory. I'd be back to where I was 30 years ago, plus, I'd be in good company now because there are so many more overweight people than in the 1980s and even the 90s.

I'd say to everyone, "Is this better? Do you prefer that I'm back at 380? Do you feel better about me now? Do you feel better about yourself when you're around me?"

Yes, I may still hold some rage about how awful it was to grow up fat. Sadly, a whole bunch of that rage is directed towards myself because I let it happen. We're ultimately responsible for our fat, though it doesn't feel it at the time. I thought it was the world doing it to me.

But it was the only way I had to cope. This helps me to forgive myself. I even start to feel pretty proud of myself for surviving. Eating kept me alive all those years. So, thank you, fat, for helping me make it to the point where I could sort through all the crap and do things differently.

This forgiveness settles me down and even helps me need food less. I even start to feel a certain confidence that I will remain thin. I ponder, how many elderly, overweight people do we see? In a mall somewhere, I saw a giant scale that you could slip a quarter into and step on and get your weight, and also your fortune. Fat wins in the end, first by making us sad and then killing us, so I continue the constant pursuit of staying under 180 pounds.

## The binge before the rebound

If I've had a stretch of eating candy, cookies, too much popcorn, and caramel-flavored mini puffed rice cakes (a favorite because the crunch helps chew out nervousness), it will be time to get back to sane eating. But a brief binge is a glorious last hurrah.

Hubby was gone for a few days for work, and this particular binge was going to be a good one. I could feel the adrenaline rise like the night before Christmas as a kid. Eating ice cream and puking it up would have done it in the old days, but it wasn't an option anymore. It hurts, it makes me feel stuffed for weeks, it plugs up my ears and nose, and it gives a constant sore throat. It literally eats away the esophagus, and if that can't make a person stop, what will? I remind myself of these awful things, because the thought still enters my head. That bulimia went away, pretty much on its own, has been one of the biggest bullets I've dodged in my life, though it unnerves me that the idea of it skitters across my mind to this day. It seems like the deal of the century until the teeth start falling out and the esophagus tears.

A binge before getting back on the wagon is sort of like bingeing and purging, but without the damage to your throat and teeth and psyche. You get the release without the side effects. When a binge happens the day before healthy eating ensues, it feels like a hall pass. You get all the fun with no guilt.

There is nothing so glorious to me as a night of untethered eating. It's kicking back at happy hour when you no longer have booze in your life. It's hiring a hooker to pretend you're someone else (I would imagine!). A great, blissed-out binge can only happen the night before getting back on track. It's the emotional eater's bachelor party in Vegas where everything lives in secret.

This slanted view may always be with me. It's management of the problem, not solving it. It's doing the best that I can because most of us fat kids never really, truly, completely get over this, I believe. For me, it's ongoing. It's a daily task of trying to feed the good beast rather than the bad, but playing with the bad beast from time to time in a controlled way. Then I put him back in his cage before he mauls me.

When a binge is planned for the night, I don't eat much during the day. It's like the idea alone gives me so much comfort.

> **It's something so good to look forward to, which is my secret to happiness. Crafting things to look forward to is my happiness formula, but on a larger scale than a binge.**

A binge on an empty stomach is like drinking coffee first thing in the morning. It hits so strong and pure, and at 3 p.m. on this particular day, the eating witching hour for me, I had my first little candy bar. "Well, here I go," I said out loud.

Every food party has an emotional theme. I know the type of food I need according to what I feel is missing or what is throbbing in my insides on a given day. This day, I needed something gooey and warm and slightly sweet to lift me up a little, but a touch savory to ground the circuits. If I could have anything, I thought, it would be a giant bowl of sweet apple crisp with a crunchy oatmeal and butter and brown sugar top, with whipped cream, and lots of it, so I found my way to the grocery store.

The drive there is full of anticipation, like the week before a vacation. It's almost the best part. It's all good feelings about the food, and because I'll be getting on track the next day, there's no need for the pesky guilt and remorse. It's the feeling of driving along the highway with the windows open and Sheryl Crow singing "Soak Up the Sun."

Cub Foods and I have this strangely intimate, dysfunctional relationship. It's my enabler. It calls to me, and I roam the aisles with my basket like Dorothy carried, but this time I was having trouble landing on something. It was like I had a parrot on my shoulder squawking in my ear phrases like: "No, that will make you feel terrible," "You don't need this to feel good," and "This is bad for you."

There was a big blueberry pie slice sitting in a plastic triangle with a pop-up clam shell lid that found its way into my basket. It was on clearance which made it more appealing; it makes no sense to spend a lot on food that goes in so quickly you don't even taste it. When I got home, I warmed it in the microwave and dropped a softball of sugar-free Cool Whip on top that melted into a liquid that looked like the grease in the bottom of a pan of roasted chicken. One of the blueberries in the pie had heated up so much that when I bit it, it exploded and burnt the roof of my mouth.

What a sad little event it ended up being. My taste buds were so numb from the yogurt-covered pretzels and rice crackers I inhaled on the way home in my car, it was all an anonymous blob going down. No sparks flew. It was a masturbation session when you're expecting torrid sex.

The party fell flat. It reminded me of going to a cast party for a play I wasn't in. Those were always hellish. If you're not in the cast, you might as well be a piece of furniture. No one wants to talk to you unless you are part of the play, and you end up sitting in the kitchen with all the other not-so-special people.

I was ready to start fresh the next day. I was lucky. Pigging out was starting to have the candy shop effect. I'd heard once that in the old days in France when girls were first hired to work the counters and back rooms of candy shops, bosses would let them eat their fill. They could have as much as they wanted, and soon the candy repulsed them. My candy shop effect took 40 years.

## Beginning again: The first day of skinny eating

Overeating, particularly to the point where my belly feels like it could split, creates a chemical effect in my body I can feel. Like drugs and alcohol, the high is undeniable. It's a drugged-out numbness and a wave of bliss and escape, which I remember more than the awful regret, so I keep going back.

Coming down from it zaps all my energy though. The hangover is like an alcohol one with scattered, manic thoughts and subtle shakes. A scratchy fogginess fills my head like I had two bottles of wine, but with less of a headache.

> **I'm hopeful about getting back on the wagon but panicked that I can't have my treats anymore. How will I get through the day without my little sugar bumps?**

From experience, that wears off, though it takes a few days. In half a week, eating an apple instead of trail mix in my truck on the way home from the grocery store comes easy. No longer will I think I can have a doughnut at the gas station. I'll still wish I could, but reason takes over.

So, here I go, and I ride on the adrenaline as the excitement of finally, and yet again, doing something about the insane eating takes over. The hope of all this craziness finally ending is my everything at that moment as I begin to roll the boulder up the mountain once more.

Dieting itself can be an addiction. I've been on a diet every day of my life; I assure you, I am on one today as you read this. Like all addictions, it gives you hope to latch onto, which I think is at the core of addiction. But my dieting addiction at least keeps me in the mindset of moderate eating. When I don't think of a day as a diet, an eating frenzy is waiting at the back door.

But starting over again with eating that is cleaner, brighter, and perhaps healthier, brings clarity to the day. There's a welcome order in reestablishing food boundaries and feeding my body better. It feels kinder. I notice I'm less bothered by little stressors when I eat this way. Because I am finding order and control within myself, things I have no control over matter less. I'm easier to be around when I eat like this.

After enough returns to sane eating, and hopefully because of the inner work I've done, I've come to have moments like this: I'll look at some blob of fat on my leg and start to chastise it, but then I catch myself. I'll tell it: "You poor little thing, what you've been through." I begin to have real compassion for my body and the marathon I've forced it to run. It's been a triathlon of abuse, remorse, and recovery done over and over.

> **Each return to sane eating is a fresh start and I'm full of optimism that the sane days will smother out the crazy ones.**

What would my body be if not subjected to all my wicked trickery? What weight would I settle down to when I'm not shoveling it full of food and I'm moving in the way my body wants to, with dancing, gardening, and lots of walking?

In your 50s, it's the body that rules all. The body begins to make the choices. I've heard it said you have the face at 50 you deserve, which is a rather harsh statement. I have a body that is the sum total of many years of extra weight and generalized self-abuse. 380 at 18, then I spent the larger part of my 20s at 280, then 200 by the time I was in my early 30s, and the 170s in my 40s. I have played around with gaining and losing 10 pounds since then.

I work at staying near 170 pounds; this is how I can somehow say sorry to my body and my inner self. Maybe I can make things right by completely ridding myself of any excess weight and any food that isn't good for me. Not one extra pound on my poor put-upon frame, my knees having fared the worst since first getting pushed down the stairs in high school. I have a baby tooth sized bone chip that floats around my lower leg reminding me of the day. I imagine my left knee has grown extra tendons, to prop up my body.

Should my knees ache so, and then I wonder, oh dear, do I have one of those bodies that is meant to be about 165 pounds or even less? Insurance company weight charts suggest that some bodies are meant to be that low. I guess the way you get to where your body is meant to be is to eat only when you are hungry, and to feed it only what it nutritionally needs to run, which is as big a mystery to me as to how to throw a football.

Food will never be in my life under those limited terms. In my world, food is a clingy teenage boyfriend, a co-worker who overshares, and an uncle who brushes up behind me with a hard-on at a family reunion. Food is a diva. It's Judy Garland, who I've read was equal parts the best, most loving friend in the world and the biggest, neediest pain-in-the-ass you could imagine.

So, I give food a night, or maybe a week or two, of the food tango. I'll have my occasional indulgences to give food the attention he demands, to keep him happy, and not wreak havoc on my life too greatly. We'll have an intermittent affair. I will love him, celebrate him, kiss him, flatter him, and invite him to enter me. He'll explode in my mouth and excite me. Then I end the affair yet again, and we become "just friends."

> **When faced with some of the painful effects of years of extra pounds and all the mindless, crazy eating, it becomes a pressing issue to treat your body like nothing else matters; in the end nothing else does. It's certainly more important than being concerned with what others think.**

## The realities of getting back on the wagon

When I begin a skinny eating day after a big eating period, I'm often antsy and depressed. I'm also scattered because these are all the things that food helps me with. The hope that this time will be different carries me through what are basically the DTs.

The mornings aren't so bad because everything is so fresh and new, and

I can look forward to lunch. In the first half of the afternoon, I have no genuine hunger pangs. Surprisingly, I still have them; all the overeating hasn't completely killed my body's signals. Plus, the psychic buildup of the day hasn't knocked me off center yet.

Then three o'clock comes, and this begins the stretch when the whole day can go to hell. Any extra weight on my body happens from 3 to 6 p.m.

**I think we overweight folks can link our weight to a few specific hours in the day.**

The workday winds down, and an itch sets in. It's the bumpy transition from work to personal life, and the evening looms ahead. Happy hour numbs the itch but when the "happiness" wears off, the itch is worse.

So, how do I get through that deadly 3 to 6 period? I plan my work so that it's not so computer-focused and more free-form and creative. I use my hands. I clean and brighten my office. I take photos. I write. I will white knuckle it a little, but generally, I will try to lighten my outlook and engage myself in something specific, creative, and physical. I will do whatever I can to not eat.

I get outside as soon as possible because that instantly short-circuits the mania. And I'll friendly binge a little if I need it.

Then the evening sets in. No matter what fun I have planned or how many loved ones surround me, why does the nighttime stretch before me so cavernous and lonely? It hearkens back to my teen years when the nighttime meant it was time to start dreading what the next day would bring. The only thing that makes it less lonely is the heavenly feel of eating and eating and eating and of course, drinking, too.

It's time to let that association go and claim the evening as the time I'm in control of. I own it and can make it anything I want. The same goes for the next day; tomorrow can be a great day. Thank you, higher power, that I am a grown-up now, and I swear, I wouldn't go back and relive those early days for a billion dollars. I worry about all the fat little gay boys out there suffering as I did, and I hope they have someone looking out for them.

Eating a light dinner, or supper as we called it on the farm, and then eating almost nothing from then until bed, this was a major part of my losing weight through the years. Now that I'm pretty much at my weight for life, it might be the biggest thing that keeps me there. When I want to eat at night to relieve a little of the anxiety that always creeps in, I remind myself that I can eat tomorrow; I can even eat a lot tomorrow, but I can't eat tonight. I remind myself nothing is worth me eating, because nothing is as important as my peace and happiness and staying thin and healthy. Everything works out better if I don't emotionally eat at night.

## Born hungry

I may have just been born hungry—forever hungry for love and pretty much anything I can get my hands on. Because of my family and its natural slant towards eating, I discovered that food seemed to fill the hole I felt inside. Instead of hugs and sharing, we had mashed potatoes whipped up and set in front of me. They were dependable and delicious and warm and smooth and fun and good. I'd immerse myself into a plate of them, like some kids did with Legos, and who wants that to end? I wanted more and more. I wanted more potatoes, and I wanted more and more love. A life away from the plate just didn't feel good. It was scary and unpredictable.

Then the fat piled on and I got teased endlessly for it. Then I heard fag as well as fatso, so I thought for it to be okay for me to be here, and I mean on this earth, I needed to change everything about myself. That's what kept me feeling safe. I did what I needed to do because the world felt like an episode of *Survivor*. Perhaps things went this way so I could learn to find it on my own.

I want to forever be done with this self-torture, this eternal act of trying to be something that the world will accept. All the self-abuse, guilt, shame, and emotional craziness need to go away for good.

Why does the self-sabotage still take over? It remains an anxiety born of a panicked, people pleasing reaction to fear and insecurity.

**Disappointing someone, anyone, including society in general—
and also myself—causes me to turn to food.**

In a sentence, that's what it comes down to. Growing up, I always felt like a
big fat letdown to everyone. Now, I still struggle with firm confidence in my
own thoughts and feelings. I still have other people's positions too much in
mind.

I confess that I sometimes use all this as an excuse for avoiding the things I
dream of in my life. Trying new things is hard. Doing things you care deeply
about is scary because the price of failure is higher. It requires being bad at
first, and that scared me so much as a little kid. They'll all make fun of me,
and I'll look like just a dumb little fat boy. Being a fat, femmy little picked-on
kid stalled my emotional development and sent me stumbling through the
life of an adult with the emotions of a child.

How could I have not tried desperately to please people as I grew up in order
to survive, and to make my way in the world and fit in? But people pleasing is
like a tick that sinks in and sucks your true self out of you and gives you the
disease to please, as it has been coined.

**When I've had a return to bingeing for a while, I'm reminded that
my food addiction hinges on this: I care too much about what
others think of me and I seek emotional comfort because of the
disappointment I feel from them.**

And I have to mention, the things we get addicted to are so dang pleasurable,
how can we not get hooked? At the very honest core of my food addiction
might also be the fact I love food. I love to eat.

So, how do I finally—and I mean finally—settle into a contented life? A life
where I can finally feel at home inside myself.

**Because that's what it's all about. To feel at home in one's own skin.**

For so long, life was all about getting to 180 pounds; then I could finally figure out all the mysteries of living, and poof, I'd be happy.

Finally, I made it to 180 by way of decades of what felt like living in a blender. I had lost 200 pounds, and I swore on the proverbial stack of Bibles I would never be fat again.

Life is now easier and all around better. I am so much happier, but 180 pounds didn't give me immunity to my insecurities as I had expected. When I lost the weight, I kept exposing myself more it seemed, as if my shirt was unbuttoned and I was getting ready for surgery on my weird, porous heart.

As great as being 170 is, this whole weight loss game of first losing and then trying to stay thin feels like I'm still just trying to feel right in the world. Being thin helps me not stand out. It helps me walk the world without being noticed because a part of me still equates being noticed to being humiliated. To be seen is to be the butt of jokes.

What I still really, really want is to be myself and completely fit in.

**And finally, I realized, I don't want to fit in. What I want most is to be myself and feel safe. To fit in and feel safe inside my own heart. That's the only way to "fit in." This I can do on my own, without the approval of others, but a higher power does help.**

I can do this. Farm boys are tough little bastards, I remind myself. Even when we are gentle little flowers, we survive. We figure it out. We are barn cats. You can throw us out of the hay loft, as I'm ashamed to say we did to many a cat, and we land on our feet. We had 25 cats at a time, and they would sleep with the cows and drink the discarded milk that had blood in it, and sometimes a wave of distemper would clean out most of the clowder, but they'd work their way back. They were always there.

I may not be the most ambitious person in the world. I admit that at my core I'm happiest sitting in a field of blooming alfalfa, searching for shapes in the clouds. I want to be fine with that because, ugh, this unending internal pursuit to be something is like constantly carrying groceries up four flights of stairs. I'm so tired of the fight to get a gold star from society. I've lived it since fifth grade when I ran for class president.

Some people seem to own it without trying. I see it all around. What is it they have? Confidence, a seemingly magical way with all life things, and a general sense of just killing it in their corner of the world. They say "fuck it" to everything that doesn't fit them, as I dream of doing, but it's such a natural part of who they are, it doesn't come off rude or nasty. Their "fuck its" sound genuine and spontaneous.

What is it I think I want anyway? What is this lack in me, this giant hole that needs to be constantly filled? To be famous? Recognized on a grand scale? To be adored and have people look at me in awe and think I'm really something? Was I born with this need for celebrity of sorts, or am I trying to make up for lost time when I felt like crap as a little kid? It's like I'm trying to get from others what I can't give myself. I'm saying to all the haters through the years—or most likely, just the ones from junior high and high school—look at me now. I seem to have these latent aspirations to be a major Fonzie out in the world, just so amazing and admired and legendary.

That's not what I want when I settle myself down and take deep breaths like my voice teachers taught me in college. When I wipe my face down with an emotional cold wet washcloth like Mom did when I got manic, I know I want to feel all these golden things about myself but without the need for the spotlight shining on me.

People do think we are rock stars, even when we don't hear the applause. One day I was reading on the front porch as two power walkers stopped in front of our house, and they went on and on about my front yard garden that I pour so much of myself into. I hid and listened like I did when I was six, and company came over. If I hadn't happened to be sitting where I was, I would have never heard and then never felt the emotional high it gave me. If we feel good and proud of something we've done, someone else is probably feeling it, too.

I step outside myself and see I am two people: My grown-up self and the

12-year-old fat boy who is scared to death.

It's time to go back and get the little fat boy. Maybe the fact that he still lives in me is why I can't completely get rid of the compulsive, emotional eating. He is still hiding in me, but I can go back and get him. I am happy to carry him; he is still very scared, but we can join forces now. I can take care of him because I've passed 50, and there's no more time to waste.

I say to my 12-year-old, we are going to be fine now. We don't give a damn about other people's shit. We're going to live on our terms, following our own heart. The junior high boys can't hurt us. They could be dead or methed out or perhaps most ironically beautiful—very fat. We're fit now. We can outrun them.

Yes, I am stuck at 12, and when I say that to myself, the voice in my head is high in my throat, and I sound like I'm asking permission. This makes my heart sink an inch in my chest.

So, I go back via my mind's eye, and I begin punching and yelling. I sneak up on the bullies from behind, and I kick them to the ground and jump on top of them, and I don't want to do anything so violent as cripple them, but they should at least want to run. This is not the 50-something Eric beating up the junior high thugs. This is the seventh-grade Eric showing them what he's got. 50-something Eric just drove and dropped him off at the field behind the school and is standing nearby.

Beating up is the term I use because that is the term that we used in 1979 Arlington, Minnesota. Eric is letting them know that they can't fucking do what they did. They can't wipe their shoes on my painter's pants or spit on my head or grab my brand-new orange wet comb out of my side pocket and break it in half. They can't push me down the stairs and scream, "Fuckin', faggot." They can't take trumpet valve oil and fling it at the back of my new blue satin jacket. Yes, I know, the clarinet is a girl's instrument, as they've made clear, so I will switch to the saxophone to hopefully be less of a fat, sissy target, plus the saxophones were in front of the kinder trombone section. Also, to those who stole my PE. clothes at the end of tenth grade, I want them back, or you can pay me the $35, you choose, and I know who you are, though one of you is dead. Shitheads.

It's not enough to just go back to this awful time and get little Eric and tell him it's okay. I need to go back and help him kick some ass. Take no prisoners, as they say. Make them bleed.

Then it's time to go. I leave it all in the past as I blow a kiss to the shitheads, which is a form of forgiveness. It's a gesture that says what you did was wrong and cruel, but I understand. You were very mean, but you were just a bunch of kids, young and dumb. Then we walk out of the gym, the locker room, and the school's front doors with a swagger, like the boy who scored the winning point at the basketball game.

I relinquish the bad feelings I felt at the time and that I've held on to. I trade them in for strength and courage and a right to breathe and to have a solid place in the world. I see there's nothing fundamentally wrong with me. This mojo was lying in wait, pent up, and it's got a ton of glory within it.

I can live life and be myself now. I can be creative and independent and fun and expressive and even though I'm a fairy, I can have all the things that straight people can have like a home and car and marriage and kids and not live a crazy, addicted life. We all need to sing "Don't Rain on my Parade," from *Funny Girl* a lot. I recommend everyone to download it and sing it in the car at full voice as often as you can, but stick with the original Barbra Streisand version.

> **It compels me to say again: You can do anything you want in life, as long as you... fill in the blank. This is the secret. Be kind and respectful of others. Be responsible, as in do what you must to pay your bills and be a good citizen and all that. If you let yourself do what you really want in life, you don't need the food or booze or shopping or lottery tickets or whatever distracts and numbs. Do what you need to do to be able to do what you really want. Quite simply, do it or die. I think the things we truly want are the things we are put on this earth to do.**

Added bonus, you're not such a pain to other people. Years later on the other side, I still get trapped in the thinking that I have to do or be a certain way.

That I can't risk doing what I really want in life. But when people don't tend to their own emotional garbage, their self-esteem needs and such, they are tough on the people around them. They are challenging to partners, lovers, family, friends, co-workers, and even to the world as a whole.

# Chapter 18

## Are you there, God? It's me. A compulsive eater.

C ompulsive eating, binge eating, emotional eating, mindless eating, generalized crazy eating—I wish I could write about getting past it all without talking about God. I say that because so many hate the G-word.

People have strong reactions to the word God. "I don't believe in religion" or "I don't go to church" are a couple of common responses. I know where these come from. I've been there, and I am there. God, church, and religion are the same in the collective mind, and it's a reaction to the general yuck from the mouths of some Christians (self-declared) and the years of confusion, constriction, and generally feeling like hell in church.

We think that to believe in God is to give in to "them." If we do, the big old Catholic or Lutheran or Methodist church then succeeds in making us be a certain way. We think to believe in God is to succumb to the brainwashing. It's to forever live in the first communion dresses and confirmation gowns and to confess our sins and wait for the church people to tell us we're okay.

Then there is the big question which no one has an answer to: If there is a God, why do babies get cancer and innocent college kids get murdered and the most horrible of horrible things happen constantly? Why are there thousands of people starving to death in one part of the world when we are throwing away slightly old produce in another? Why do people with ridiculously big guns kill grade school kids?

It can seem like "he" (God) is evil and is up there in heaven on his throne in his flowing man caftan, combing his long white beard and taking random shots at us down here. I used to see God as a heaven-based sniper. Unless I went to church and declared that I was a Christian and an unwavering believer—and not gay—I could be the next to get shot. Worse yet, even if I threw myself at the mercy of the church and God, bad things would still happen.

I thought I had to plead with God, and he would decide if I was worthy. God was a straight, crew-cut football coach who would never give me a second look because I was so fat and femmy and couldn't throw a ball. He (for sure he) was the ruler of all things and all people, and he lived way up there in heaven, and I had to figure out how to please him. How was I ever going to feel a straight white man was on my side? None of them championed me, but to be fair, a couple actually did. Mr. Moore, my high school drama and English teacher who looked like Jesus in twentieth-century paintings, was an Eric-advocate. Paster Grant, our Lutheran minister who finished off the leftover communion wine with my dad, was a good guy, too. But I was overwhelmed by the bullying ones. They looked at me like I was bird poop on their Corvette.

There was no way God could be like them and also be my helper, my protector, and my partner. I was looking for a savior, and it needed to be someone who could feel my pain, and God just didn't seem like a compulsive eater. If I was to have a higher power at work in my life—someone who had my back and would look out for me and be there when I asked for help—it couldn't be someone who I thought would ultimately reject me.

How beautiful it would be if I could shift my thoughts from who I thought God was—a vindictive white man who hated and judged me and thought I was a disgusting little fat, femmy hayseed—and think of him or her or it as something or someone who was on my side. What if this being was always there for me?

The closest I've gotten to making sense of it all is to see God as a big ball of energy in the general shape of a person, rather than an actual person. I think of God as inside and around and woven through us all, and we can dial into him (or her or it) to help us try to make sense of all the craziness here on earth. I think God has a landline phone that's always answered, though sometimes you must leave a message that takes a while to be returned, but it always is. When I add that everything happens for some reason in a master plan of sorts, I can live with the mystery of it all.

What if God isn't what we, or at least I, always thought? What if God is everything we ever need to get through this thing called life, to quote Prince? And God doesn't have anything to do with all the churches and priests and choirs and communion wafers and organs groaning or really anyone or anything on the earth plane? I never have to set foot in a church or declare myself a Christian to put my trust in God. This is the only kind of God I want to believe in, and I need to believe that something is out there.

**I ask, why was it forever so difficult for me to connect to something spiritual?**

Here's a piece of my theory: When you grow up fat, you are very aware of your body. People are always referring to it. "Boy, he's a little porkchop. You like to eat, don't you? Oh, look at the little football player." This makes you very aware of your body—overly aware—and I began to think that the body was everything. My brain and heart and soul and everything inside had no say. My inner world had no power or voice. My thoughts and feelings, when fully expressed, just got me into trouble, so it was all about the body. I was only my body. I was responsible for it, which I was, and I really screwed up.

That's why I had trouble connecting to any sort of greater spiritual presence. I was so into using my five senses to make sense of the awful world, I could never get in touch with my sixth sense, which is the only way to feel a spiritual presence, or God, if you will.

I lived entirely in the physical world. I sat all alone with the body I created and was ashamed of it, and I felt all alone. No one was there to help or take care of me, and the ignoring was a form of punishment for being a bad boy. Prayer was pointless. Hopefulness just got dashed the next day in PE.

**I then found myself in adulthood, not tapping into anything beyond the five senses and cut off from tuning into any type of inner compass.**

It was all about the body. The fat pile I built and I sat in.

A shift happened that wasn't like getting struck by lightning or touching the electric fence on the farm. It was quite the opposite.

After sitting in church for what I estimate to be over 1,000 hours, a bit of spiritual truth may have seeped in around the edges, so the potential for some inspiration was there. All the logged pew time accumulated to where I could feel it a little when I got quiet and thought optimistically about all God could be and do for me in my life. Maybe the voice of the real God was working on my subconscious all those years, like the subliminal weight loss tape I had tried. This God was also likely screaming in churches everywhere, "Come on people, get with the program!"

Then I listened to hours of new age spiritual types on Hay House radio, the spiritual publishing company. I listened at work all day and to audiobooks while I drove. These bits and pieces worked their way in as well.

My cells shifted slowly, more glacier than avalanche. All the talk that God wasn't someone but more a force of good and love and infused into all of us made sense. I started to feel he could be in and around me, on my side and there to help.

I'm also repelled a little by the G-word. When I use the term higher power, a wave of good feelings come over me, though I still use God and higher power interchangeably. When I think about a higher power helping me whenever I need it, I feel the comfort I go to food for.

It helps me to see God as a man. It repairs my general terror of straight men. I imagine God as tall and beautiful and strong and brave (though more like a large, marble statue of David, than an actual man), and he loves me like a dog loves its owner. He jokes with me, hugs me, and tells me I am perfect and wonderful exactly as I am, even in holey socks and eating a bowl of cereal over the sink. He goes with me everywhere, like a father or big brother, and he protects me. He wards off the mean people and handles rude waiters and devious car repairmen.

This is what I ask God for, above all: Give me the self-confidence and the personal power to love and be fair and kind and rock-solid no matter what anyone does or says to me. Then maybe I won't need to turn to food and drink.

This God nudges me in the right direction when I am confused. When I ask what I can do in return, all he says is live your best life and keep asking for help. Just imagine if this is what God is really like. A relationship with a higher power can be the most important thing in our lives... and it has nothing to do with church or religion.

Could it be we are presented with challenges like addictive behavior to get to know a higher power and to learn to ask for help?

**We don't need to do it all alone. Some days, I go moment by moment asking my higher power to get me through each challenging thought, each compulsion to go get trail mix, and this is how I finally, finally got to know him. I have no proof—no one does—but I believe with all my heart that we all have him, her, or them on our side, helping us every second.**

"Dear higher power, ignite feelings of safety and belonging in me that I have to believe are my birthright," I whisper to myself. This is who I think God is: he's a something that is woven through everyone and everything, like gold threads in my mom's old plaid Christmas tablecloth. God is like the coils that run through a heated floor. They are sunk into cement or laid under the hardwood and then turned on with the thermostat, and then the energy, the heat, and the surge of power cruises through the coils and warms the place up.

God is like a sunny day. God is the feeling I get when "Walking on Sunshine" comes on the radio when I'm driving down the road with the windows open on a warm, bright Friday afternoon.

# The wind reminds me

I love the wind. It's an invisible force of magic from somewhere. Sometimes still, it's the only way I can feel there is something bigger out there that protects me. The wind is more tangible than God, and that helps so much. I'm lucky because the wind sort of flicks my forehead to remind me that I'm not required to do this all by myself. Bigger forces are at play. Something or someone is "out there" to help. I still have flashes of doubt there is a God, and when I do, I can trust the power of nature and the universe, and the wind helps me remember. Leaves blowing past my back door speak to me. Nature elements like wind and trees and flowers are very God-like.

# Plus, I think I have a hot, movie star guardian angel

It was one of those blah mornings I know everyone has as I sat between bed and work and just looked around. It's usually a grey and overcast day when this happens to me, and all I could think was, is this all there is? Is life just about going to blah, boring work where everyone is bitching? I prayed, which I finally taught myself to do despite years of doubting it in Sunday School, confirmation class, and church.

I did pick up a few tips about prayer along the way in church. I learned from all the old ladies with lots of perfume and beautiful sparkly earring and brooch sets. I stared endlessly at their rhinestones, and they would seem to sink into these deep trances with their brows furrowed and heads tilted to the side, all pleading and forlorn and like they were thinking, "Oh dear heavenly father, deliver me from the suffering of this awful world."

This is the type of praying I have finally landed on. For years, I tried to make my prayers reasonable, like a negotiation at the car dealership, and I didn't want to be a bother or ask too much or seem ungrateful, like a true Minnesotan. Now I just spill my guts and dump it all out there. I throw myself at the mercy of the court of my higher power. I risk being unreasonable in my requests. I've come to know my higher power can handle it.

That's how I prayed that morning, and I asked God to be with me that day.

> **I asked to connect to my poor angels, who have had a hard, thankless job for decades, and I got "the feeling."**

I had felt a spiritual presence in the past but chalked it up to a good caffeine buzz. This was a different, deeper feeling. It was warm and calm and clear. It was the feeling after a glass of wine, but with an alert mind.

My head was bowed, and I was sitting in my kitchen with only the under-cabinet lights on, which made the room glow as if lit by candles. There seemed to be a certain something in the room, and I felt like someone was looking at me. I swore I could even hear the floor creak. I was terrified to lift my head. I've sensed it before at times throughout my life, but I always thought it was mean boys getting ready to pounce.

I finally looked up, and there was a giant dude in my kitchen, like a professional football player angel standing in a pose that said, "I am here to serve you." Writing about it gives me the chills. I have a hot angel on my side, I thought. He was a movie star angel. A divine, celestial Jason Mamoa. This angel who was in front of me seemed very real. I felt he'd always been there and that he always would be. With him by my side all day, what's to be afraid of? I don't recall if he had wings, but he must have because he had the general angel swagger to him.

When I worry about a meeting where I may have my neck on the chopping block, he is with me. I send him in first, and whatever happens, he is there. Plus, if Jason Mamoa angel wants to hang out with me, I must be sort of a rock star, badass, spiritual being as well.

4 p.m. comes, and I want candy. There are M&Ms at the reception desk, and all I can think about is the little crack that comes when I bite into one, and then the sweet milk chocolate center hits me. They soothe the hard edges (but all they really do is open a floodgate). Jason Mamoa angel, he knows what I need. He has my back. I dial into him. Texting and e-mail work, too, but calling is best. How does it help? I don't feel so alone. I feel like I have

help. Plus, hopeful thoughts somehow play in my head when I remember he is there, like a Viewmaster clicking through beautiful images.

# VI

# Part Six

*Goodbye, Mom*

# Chapter 19

## Mom and I say our earthly goodbyes

When my mom appeared to be in the final days of her life and barely spoke, I made her caramels on the stovetop. I boiled sugar, milk, vanilla, and baking soda and timed them to get the perfect softness that would be easy for her to eat because her teeth didn't allow for much chewing any longer. She gestured to the old Christmas cookie tin I packed them in. She maneuvered the cover off like a pro, and those things are tough to get off. She reached in and smeared out a soft caramel. She not so much ate it as applied it to her tongue, and she got the closest to a smile I'd seen in a long time.

> **I knew that look. It was what all of us who depend on food get when the sweetness, fat, and salt land in the right spot. Fleeting endorphins spread like a drop of food coloring in water.**

For the last five years of her life, she was hooked to an oxygen tank and had poorly fitting false teeth, and these two things left her without her two best friends, her true loves in life—cigarettes and food. She ate just enough to stay alive, but the fun was gone, along with the taste. She blamed her dentures, which I understood. The plastic piece that held all the teeth in place covered the roof of her mouth, eliminating that lovely textural experience one gets from rolling ice cream, better-than-sex cake, or buttered mashed potatoes all over with your tongue. Like me, Mom was a full-on, five-sensory eater. I remember at six years old, I watched with open mouth her altered state while she communed with a giant bowl of popcorn cooked on the stovetop in Wesson oil, with melted butter, and a ton of salt.

In her later years, she had a few foods she'd latch onto and not let go; these were her buddies. Marzetti's coleslaw dressing was her happy sauce. I walked in on her spooning it straight into her mouth, sitting in front of the fridge, and because I've been in that state and that posture a million times, it barely phased me. I greeted her as always, "Well, morning, Shirley," and gave her a little hug and unpacked the bag of groceries I had picked up. I've eaten doughnuts out of the trash at work. Raw bacon out of the fridge at home. Unknown bits off the kitchen floor. You get no judgment from me, Mom.

## When it was time for her to go

I had gone to the gym to do the elliptical machine as I had long been in the habit of doing. Fifteen years of endless climbing in search of weight loss. I then stopped at Cub Foods to get a doughnut. It was nothing fancy, a plain cake doughnut, which is the perfect little healthy/not healthy treat. It's barely sweet, with just a little whiff of grease, and the wonderful slight crunch coating and the softness when bitten is still a little hug. It's even better with coffee, and it makes the coffee better, too.

I needed a little softness to prepare for the drive back home to see Mom. I had thought she would never die. She could lock her jaw, scrunch up her face, unplug, and then be okay. She'd disassociate and disconnect from the present with that distant stare, those eyes that are open but shut off. She'd tighten up her body, turning the whole thing on the offensive, and create an emotional armadillo shell, and she'd make it through. But this time was different.

Holy shit, what was that over my left shoulder? It was like a giant bird flew through her hospital room. A terra-dactyl of white light soared in over my left shoulder, dipped over her body, then left through the wall behind

216

her head, and they were both gone. It felt like the time I was working in the garden and a hawk scooped down and snatched up a chipmunk. It was as if winged monkeys carried her off like Dorothy. It was so bright and real and big and angel-like.

"Oh, is that it?" my sister asked. And it was. Mom was gone. She had left the earth. Her body was there, but was so very, very still, small, and hollow like a log. All that made her so Mom-like was off to the next chapter, and Mom was so much bigger than a human body could contain. It all made sad sense.

Oh, Mom.

You just wanted to be loved and taken care of, didn't you? Like we all do.

When the coroner wheeled her away, she had a patchwork quilt draped over her. He had tried to avoid running into me, but I was at the vending machines in the hall, of course, getting Funyons and a Coke Zero, the one that tastes like cinnamon and is so yummy. I yelled, "Goodbye, Mom," and her body was so tiny, finally, under the quilt. She was the size of a Golden Retriever. We both had the same ultimate dream in life—to be skinny—and Mom, we finally did it. I thought you would live until you were 110, but here the day was, and there you went.

We held Mom's funeral a week later on Valentine's Day. "Shirley was fun. Shirley loved color," I said in my talk. "Shirley was my best friend when I was little. For many years, she was my only friend." The church was full. Eighty-some years on the earth, and Mom had massed a decent-sized throng of people who felt the same as I did.

I drove out of Gaylord that night, and it was dark and cold, and dark and cold in February in Minnesota is as lonely as it gets. I remember a similar feeling when Dad died, but this time as my PT Cruiser rolled northeast along Highway 5, the artery that runs from my current to my past life, I felt like I was leaving Gaylord and then Arlington and then Sibley County and then southern Minnesota for the last time.

I was free, though no one had really held me captive. I was a kite on the end of a string, but I was also the one holding the string. I rose but only to a certain point, and now somehow, I let go, and wow, the sky is really blue, and the air is cool and fresh way up here. It's a constant 68 degrees with clear skies.

Don't worry, Mom. I remember how you told me not to give a damn what others think of me. And how you said I was no better and no worse than anyone else. You and Dad did well, and as I rise and figure things out and make happiness my #1 priority, I will make sure I don't get too close to the sun and burn myself. I mean, is there really a danger that any of us from southern Minnesota will get too big for our britches?

## I am not a problem to be figured out

I figured that once I solved the "problem I called Eric," my troubles would go woosh, like when the Draino kicks in or the plunger finally works. But to think of ourselves as an unsolved problem is a mental log jam. It's a spiritual clogged toilet.

Sometimes I think the self-help industry is based on this. Like the healthcare system, they really don't want people to not need them anymore. So, I've sort of gone on a diet of those as well, though I always feel better, lighter, more hopeful, less cranky, and less acutely sensitive when I regularly listen to and read the writings of my favorite spiritual gurus. I'll name a few: Nancy Levin, Sonia Choquette, Carolyn Myss, Robert Ohotto, and the granddaddy of them all, Wayne Dyer.

But they can only offer suggestions and nudges. Their words are not stripping me of all my badness and scouring my insides and getting me to the right head place and stamping me OK. Though I have to say I owe so much to spiritual-type teachers and writers. They are my higher power mentors.

It feels great to declare I am okay exactly as I am. I am right and perfect as-is. Even that hymn I sang hundreds of times in church starts to make sense. "Just as I am without one plea." I always hated it, thinking I was singing how wretched and unworthy I was and God, please love me, a huddling, shaking pile of rubble on the ground. But it actually suggests that I am okay exactly as I am. Every second is like my first second on this earth, and I am reborn perfect, but not at all perfect because that's so damned boring. I am divinely, splendidly, magnificently imperfect, and exactly the way I am meant to be. Mistakes, and imperfections, and quirks are actually the beauty, dimension, and sparkle that make us fabulous beings.

> **Imperfection makes us interesting, charismatic, and fun to be around. Other people worship people who are completely themselves (though they usually hide their ardor).**

I am not a problem that has to be fixed. None of us are. We are solutions. We are our own solutions to all the questions we have. The solutions to the problems we have really are inside us.

Sometimes we think we have problems we don't really have because we don't feel right in the world. There's a phrase that goes, "the present is perfect." I'll have days where I challenge myself to see nothing as a problem, that everything is perfect just as it is.

The changes we'd like to make in ourselves are simply adventures to embark on that help us discover even greater dimensions of our already fabulous selves. That's my story, and I'm sticking to it.

## A final shift to compassion

Recently, I had a shift; it was an internal click into place. I had gained ten pounds over the holidays, and it had been very slow to come off—slower than I'd ever experienced. It was like a winter thaw when you have a few warm days in January, then again in February, but March is epically cold, and April brings more snow and below-zero temps. The snowbank of extra weight was not melting. (People, lose the weight in your 20s and 30s, please!)

I was 183 and the needle of the scale would not budge. It was locked in place. I remember one week of really clean eating and walking and drinking plenty of water and doing my daily push-ups. I was the dieting poster boy. At the end of the week, I had gained a pound.

I looked at my flabby belly and dimply thighs and saggy boobs and thought, and even spoke out loud, the most awful and abusive things. "Disgusting, gross, fat pig" may have been mumbled.

Then in a flash, something grabbed me around the neck and shook me a little. I practically heard a voice say, "How dare you. This body has carried you to hell and back, and for years all you've done is abuse him and throw hate at him, and he defended you against the pricks who kicked and hit and spat on you and him." It was my higher power, an angel, and hopefully, my own conscience and self-awareness taking over.

After this somewhat out-of-body experience, I came to my senses. I had a moment of cruel insanity, and then the angels shook me. I came back to the present moment and thought (but my thoughts were so loud and clear it was as if I was speaking them out loud), "You can be any size, shape, or weight you want after what you've been through, body of mine." I cried a little, and I don't do that easily. I felt so sad that after all this time, I could turn on myself like that. But it felt like a genuine shift.

I eventually got back below 180 and close to 175, which is where my body seems to want to be. Every weight gain comes off slower as the years tick by.

All this self-hatred and shallow obsession over my body is insane and ridiculous. It still hangs around and rears its ugly head at times. I've always known my preoccupation with weight and appearance was not how I wanted to be, but it was so strong it wouldn't go away.

I dreamed of body acceptance throughout the years. I understand why it couldn't happen at 380 or 280 or even 220, but come on, I look pretty good now. I might be brainwashed with a little of that gay man's false idealism around the perfect body. Body perfectionism is a straight jacket that keeps you from being free and easy and having fun in life... and even just having a good day.

**But, this day marked a new beginning where I began to feel so much gratitude for my body still being in one piece after all my**

> **wicked ways I've forced on it. 80% of my body looks great, and the rest is beautiful just from its survival.**

It's taken decades to get to this point, and I now understand that maybe all the fat people who really do seem jolly and accepting of themselves have a little of this naturally woven through them. I hope they do. I'm just so thankful that I'm finally finding this in myself.

## The pea inside me

What if there is a physical thing deep inside us addicts? A little bump the size of a pea we are born with, like a third nipple, but on the inside. Some people develop it in the womb. Many don't. It's deep within many of us, but science has yet to uncover it.

Some of us get it from our mom or dad or both, and however that genetic firestorm happens, it develops and sticks. It seems to run in my family like brown eyes. It's something physical like a cyst or chemical abscess that grows like our appendix or gall bladder, but it has a psychological control and makes us an addict. It's a pea-sized addict thing, which is why a fun-sized candy bar turns into 20. A drink into 11. A quick stop at Target costs us $200. It's undeniable, and it's not our fault. It's just the pea.

When I eat a chocolate peanut cluster or a bugle, or pretty much anything sweet or salty, the pea screams, "No, don't stop, I need more." It's an angry, needy little bump.

I can deal with having the addict pea inside me. I find peace in the thought of it. Without it, I think, "Oh, Eric, you are weak and have a mental instability and just can't deal with life, can you?" I still believe those who can stop after a couple of drinks or don't want to eat a bakery clean after having one chocolate chip cookie are better than me. They know how to handle life.

I still think I should be able to eat one cookie and not turn into a creepy, crawly garbage monster or have one glass of wine and not have my body scream "Party!" But I can't. The pea theory helps me accept this.

In 1987, the year I graduated from college and set out into the world, the American Medical Association declared addiction a disease. They tell me it's something I was born with, that I have a predisposition for it. It's not a flaw, a weakness, a lameness, or an inability to deal with what's put in my path. So, it's not my fault. It's the disease I have. That's what they tell me, but I think addicts and perhaps former fat, gay kids buck the system a little and don't readily listen to medical studies. I still see it as a flaw and an inability to get my act together. If it's the pea, then it's a specific physical thing doing it. It's the same as how my trick knee causes me to limp sometimes.

The pea is specific, tangible, and easier for me to grasp. With the pea, I'm not always disappointing myself. If the pea is in there, I can't eat sugar or drink wine any more than a person with high cholesterol can eat steaks fried in butter or a diabetic can eat a doughnut. The pea is so rock solid. It's irrefutable and very real.

I think of the pea theory as plain and simple truth. If it's a universal fact, like gravity or the earth is round, then I feel like people won't judge me or think of me as weak or different. Or mostly, I won't judge myself. I just have the pea in me.

## The secret to life? Oh, wow he typed it!

Two of the most beloved and important people in my life were gone. One left very young, the result of carrying the weight of the world in his heart. I believe it exploded from the pressure. The other made it to her 80s, but her third act was plagued with the effects of her addictions, born from attempts to soothe the hard edges of life. Both struggled with their time on earth and from my perspective, they never felt right in this world. They were the two most talented, creative, interesting, and charismatic people I've ever known, and I don't think they even scratched the surface of their potential. Damn, it breaks my heart.

What seems to be the most terminal disease in the world—trying to fit in and feel right in the world—got them both. They suffered from people pleasing as well.

> **Not feeling like you fit in, and trying hard to do so, is so hard on the body and soul. Soothing yourself when you feel like you don't get the big "OK" stamp from society is a killer.**

You need to ease the pain after you've tried to fit into that tight suit of being like everybody else. Filling the expected blanks on the form of life is like wearing a constant straight jacket. Cigarettes and beer and sleeves of saltine crackers with butter spread thickly are a sort of pain reliever. They are an aspirin that only lasts until you are done with them though, and then the pain is back, and it seeks vengeance.

> **All any of us want in life is to be loved and accepted for who we are. To be able to be ourselves, fully and wholly, and without the judgment of others.**

Then it seems life can be a joyous ride. We all have the birthright to be happy, I simply have to believe it. Perhaps we addicts hear this whisper louder and clearer than anyone, but the message scrambles somehow or we have road blocks in place in our heads and hearts. We think eating cake until we can't breathe or getting drunk or shopping until we find the perfect shoes are what we do to be happy in this world, and then oops, that's a problem.

If I was to have an audience with God—which I think we all have access to at any moment—but the undeniable kind, like he is sitting in front of me and our knees are touching, I'd ask the big, $64,000 question: "What's it all about, why am I here, how can I be happy?" Yes, I'd have three questions.

I think he would whisper: "Do what you need to be happy no matter what anyone else says." To be kind, respectful, and loving to others is the subtext. That's it. That's all there is. I think he would also tell me that the ultimate way to serve him, which is a phrase I'd heard a million times in church, is to be myself and be happy.

> **How can anyone fit in and conform to this crazy world? We can only do what we must to make our own world within this world everything we want it to be. Then we won't feel the need to escape into a world of just soothing the pain.**

If my magical parents, my beautiful mom and dad with their crazy, artistic spirits had done that, they both might still be here.

# Chapter 20

## Finale

Maybe I'll never have one of those famously stupendous lives you read about. The kind you see on morning TV shows a lot and even occasionally stumble upon in real-time. The James Bond businessman who dresses in killer suits, and also volunteers at the homeless shelter. The sexy Food Network star who cooks with butter and cream and has a 32-inch waist. The friend of a friend who seems to have everything together: the looks, the career, the money, the family, the body. Do people like that truly exist? It would be so easy to say no, they don't. But yes, they actually do.

I then think, what did I do wrong? Why couldn't I ever get it together like that? But I know things are rarely as they appear. We all have our lives we present on social media, and then our real lives with all our foibles are what we live with on the daily.

I can live with having a stupendous inner life, because that's all any of us have any control over. What appears on the inside has the biggest effect on our happiness and is the only thing we can count on. To be a rock star in our own personal orbit the size of our outstretched arms will serve us best.

My life has been colorful and textured and yes, sometimes fractured. It was harder than it needed to be, mostly at the hand of myself, I'd say. Creative thinking can be used to make life lovelier and more difficult.

Things I haven't done in my life: Walked the Camino Real. Done a meditation retreat in India. Lived anywhere besides Minnesota. Rebuilt homes in a village on the other side of the earth. These are things I have not done.

What I have done is explored and exhausted every cell of my body, every crevice of my brain, every corner of every chamber of my heart. I was driven to see what was in all those places, maybe to check on boogeymen or evil spirits that might lurk within. I'm proud of the search and that I discovered no such thing was in there. What I did find was a happy, shy, scared, but jolly little creature inside. This sounds like a cartoon, but it's a picture I get in my head when I imagine opening the door to my heart. When I cleared the imaginary smoke and dust and piles of garbage, there he was, this kooky, little fuzzball with big eyes looking all hopeful and waving at me, wanting to play and be happy and have fun and enjoy life and not worry so much about what others think or say or do. Honestly, it's so real an image, it makes me tear up a little. It's amazing he survived intact after the internal war I waged on him and myself.

My body does carry battle scars. My flesh has a patina. It sports the footprints of my life as it suffers the aftermath of abuse. Skin never fully retracts after being stretched so far. Though the maroon of the stretch marks fades over time, the giant quotation marks on the skin stay, like embossments, a very similar color to the skin, but the shadows create a sort of texture, a subtle extra layer. To touch them is Braille. My story is written on my skin.

Physically speaking, Lou Ferrigno wasn't waiting for me underneath the fat as I had imagined all those years. I'm sort of a scarecrow now that all the fat is gone, which was disappointing. I have that type of fat that seems to collect under the skin. I read that saggy, crepey drapes of skin that hang, seemingly endlessly and forever after weight loss, can be bits and shreds of fat caught in the skin that weigh it down.

But I can contentedly live the rest of my life at the size that I am. When I look at photos of myself, which is the only way to be somewhat objective about how I look, I see a thin, fit man.

And again, I remind myself all the ways life is better and easier.

What big thing did I accomplish? Maybe my gravestone can read: He gained and lost 200 pounds. A whole person and then some.

Perhaps I can say I've lived two lives: The life in which I needed the food so badly and the life in which I learned how to live without it. Both were happening in me the whole time, so it's like I've lived my life with another person alongside me—a 200-pound brother or father or buddy. This makes sense. I was such a lonely kid, I created this friend, this other person, to be with me along the way.

So, of course, it was hard to let him go. And why I never completely will.

# Now it's your turn

This is my story. This is what worked for me. These are the shifts—mostly internal—that I made to lose 200 pounds and then keep them off for 20 years and counting. At this point in the story, all I want is to have given you enough to get you started on your own weight loss story that ends in you being thin and healthy and happy. It's what we all want and it's okay to want this. It's not shallow; it's the path to finding your true self.

No one can make you lose weight, but you know that. We all just have to get to the point where we've had enough. Often, it's that we get as tired of all the crazy thinking and behavior as we do of the extra weight. When that time comes, reading other people's journeys is powerful because we see we are not the "only one." It also helps to see that it can be done, even by someone like me who is a five-star emotional eater.

Being thin makes for an easier life. For me, it also makes for a happier one. Not all life's problems go away with the pounds, but a lot of them do. Overall, I find the challenges that come up easier to deal with when I am thin. I navigate the earth more easily. Much of this comes from the things I uncovered about myself and my thinking as I lost the weight. And much of it comes from how much easier life is in general at 175, rather than 380 or even 280. Literally and figuratively, I'm not dragging around a big steamer trunk with me wherever I go.

I'll close with this. Please make this a priority. Losing weight will change your life. You may have to tough your way through the first ten pounds, but after that, the good feelings will keep you going.

Lose the weight. Everything gets better when you do.

# About the Author

Eric Johnson grew up with his head in the clouds and his hands in the dirt of his family's farm in southern Minnesota. With a Bachelor's degree in Theater and English, as well as a Master of Fine Arts in Acting and Directing, he spent his 20s and 30s on stage, but now plays out the dramas of life on the page. For over 30 years he's employed the art of storytelling in non-profit communications at organizations serving families with seriously ill children, people experiencing homelessness, and the at-home gardening community. A lifelong passionate gardener, Eric is a regular contributor to *Northern Gardener* magazine, where he shares his gardening insights and invites readers to explore the beauty and drama of growing things.

Eating disorders run in his family, but so do humor, optimism, and creativity. He believes life's most rewarding moments are found in the pursuit of hobbies and passions that spark joy. Exploring one's creative side might be the most lifesaving thing we can do for ourselves.

You can reach Eric at www.emotional-eater.com.

Please take a moment to rate and review *Emotional Eater* on Amazon. He sure would appreciate it!

Made in the USA
Columbia, SC
22 July 2024

39147807R00137